CLASSIC

CRYPTOGRAMS

CLASSIC

CRYPTOGRAMS

By Leslie Billig, Shawn Kennedy,
Helen Nash, and Dorothy Masterson

Main Street
A division of Sterling Publishing Co., Inc.
New York

10 9 8 7 6 5 4 3 2 1

Published by Sterling Publishing Co., Inc.
387 Park Avenue South, New York, NY 10016
© 2005 by Sterling Publishing Co., Inc.

Material in this collection adapted from:
Mighty Mini Crypto-Quotes, © 1999 by Leslie Billig
Funny Cryptograms, © 2003 by Shawn Kennedy
Humorous Cryptograms, © 1995 by Helen Nash

Distributed in Canada by Sterling Publishing
℅ Canadian Manda Group, 165 Dufferin Street
Toronto, Ontario, Canada M6K 3H6
Distributed in Great Britain by Chrysalis Books Group PLC
The Chrysalis Building, Bramley Road, London W10 6SP, England
Distributed in Australia by Capricorn Link (Australia) Pty. Ltd.
P.O. Box 704, Windsor, NSW 2756, Australia

Printed in China

Sterling ISBN 1-4027-1673-7

CLASSIC CRYPTOGRAMS

CONTENTS

INTRODUCTION

With Hints for Solving Cryptograms

———

Cryptograms are quotations or phrases in a simple substitution code. In this book, every cryptogram is a quotation. Each letter of the quotation has been replaced by another letter. A letter is always represented by the same letter throughout the code. For example:

C	O	D	E	D		S	E	N	T	E	N	C	E	S
X	L	P	I	P		Y	I	H	M	I	H	X	I	Y

In this code, the Cs are represented by Xs, the O by L, the Ds by Ps, etc. The code will be consistent throughout the puzzle, but a different code is used for each puzzle. A letter will never stand for itself.

There are a number of things to look for that will help you crack the code. Here are some hints:

A one-letter word is always A or I. In a two-letter word, one letter must be a vowel.

A word with an apostrophe before the last letter is going to end in N'T (as in CAN'T), 'S (IT'S), 'M (I'M), or 'D (HE'D). Two letters after an apostrophe might be 'LL (WE'LL), 'VE (I'VE), or 'RE (THEY'RE).

Certain common words have distinct letter patterns. For example: DID, THAT, NEVER, LITTLE, and PEOPLE.

Some words occur over and over simply because they're so commonly written and spoken. Keep an eye out for THE, AND, NOT, YOU, and WITH, for example. In addition, look out for words ending in -ED, -ING, -LESS, -NESS, and -TION.

In these puzzles, which get harder as you go, the quotation is followed by the name of the person who said or wrote it. Often the person's name can be figured out, which will give you more letters with which to decode the quotation.

If you get stuck, there is a solving hint for each cryptogram starting on page 212, which will tell you what letter one of the code letters stands for. If you're still stumped, move on to another cryptogram and then go back to the problematic one later. Sometimes all you need is to look at it with fresh eyes. Remember,

DC LX CDUJX BPG ZPK'X JGIIHHZ, XUB, XUB LYLDK.*

Cryptograms are fun—fun to decode, and fun to uncover the nuggets of wit and wisdom and who said them. I hope you agree.

—Leslie Billig

---

*Answer to this cryptogram is on page 222.

CRYPTOGRAMS

1   QFL HCVPS PX V ANSWLCEZK

NCJVS; PQ XQVCQX QFL BPSZQL RNZ JLQ

ZT PS QFL BNCSPSJ VSW WNLX SNQ

XQNT ZSQPK RNZ JLQ QN QFL NEEPGL.

—CNHLCQ ECNXQ

• • • • • • • • • • • • • • • • •

2   COXBX TBX CVK CDGXR DI T GTI'R

ADHX VOXI OX ROKQAU IKC RNXPQATCX:

VOXI OX PTI'C THHKBU DC, TIU VOXI OX

PTI.   —GTBY CVTDI

Handwritten annotation above cryptogram 2:
THERE ARE TWO TIMES IN A MAN'S
LIFE WHEN HE SHOULD NOT SPECULATE
WHEN HE CAN'T AFFORD IT AND WHEN HE
CAN
            MARK TWAIN

• • • • • • • • • • • • • • • • •

3   MFX BH BC MFOK MO CZVL CA SAY,

MO'PO HZBY CA GO DPZXBKS, GIC MFOK

SAY CZVLH CA IH, MO'PO

HUFBWADFPOKBU?   —VBVX CAEVBK

4   LCY UWYTL LCGKU TASBL LCY
NSIGYE GE MSB'WY UGIGKU XYSXVY
VGLLVY LGKM XGYQYE SO LGNY LCTL
LCYM KYIYW OSWUYL.

—ZGNNM ELYPTWL

• • • • • • • • • • • • • • • • • •

5   JTJQCEGJQJ X AL X'B ORNJU XW
X SGXZN SGJ YZXTJQRXSC RSXWFJR
EQXSJQR. BC LMXZXLZ XR SGOS SGJC
ULZ'S RSXWFJ JZLYAG LW SGJB.

—WFOZZJQC L'KLZZLQ

• • • • • • • • • • • • • • • • • •

6   AN CBCR'Z LMM KVSN VUND VR
ZXN PLSN PXBQ, YHZ AN'DN LMM BR ZXN
PLSN YVLZ.   —YNDRLDC YLDHKX

7   ZW WPPE QS OSBSJWSSJ ISGKO
WP ASW WFKSS WFPTOGJC FZWO ZJ
LGOSLGDD. Z CZC ZW ZJ PJS GRWSKJPPJ
PJ WFS APDR UPTKOS.   —FGJE GGKPJ

• • • • • • • • • • • • • • • • • •

8   MWUCU'A TB MCRJD MB IURTN F
WPZBCRAM GWUT XBP WFKU MWU
GWBHU NBKUCTZUTM GBCDRTN EBC XBP.
                        —GRHH CBNUCA

• • • • • • • • • • • • • • • • •

9   L ENXVZ POMV UEZQ
BEZMVHGOXLEZG ALXP RTGVUN, OZJ L
OR GE BUVMVH XPOX GERVXLRVG L JEZ'X
YZJVHGXOZJ O GLZQUV AEHJ L OR
GOTLZQ.   —EGBOH ALUJV

10   MIKXCJ KCC WIM OKM ZLKMA

KAUIXZNLJ, SDL NR JGD BKML LG LIZL K

WKM'Z OTKXKOLIX, PNUI TNW VGBIX.

—KSXKTKW CNMOGCM

• • • • • • • • • • • • • • • • •

11   WLCHOBCHW BO'W MHPHWWSQJ

OL FL S ALMF ZBWOSMPH LKO LU ODH

VSJ BM LQZHQ OL PLCH NSPX S WDLQO

ZBWOSMPH PLQQHPOAJ.

—HZVSQZ SANHH

• • • • • • • • • • • • • • • • •

12   ZP YZP V EYX XY XOYIVT PJCTYB. CA

CX ZPMPB'X AYM OCI, ZP'J RP ZVXUOCBH

XPEPNCTCYB RF UVBJEPECHOX.

—ICEXYB RPMEP

13   SMLMK PMTT GMUGTM FUV PU XU

PFBSEY. PMTT PFMC VFOP PU XU OSX

PFMH VBTT YDKGKBYM HUD VBPF PFMBK

BSEMSDBPH.   —EMUKEM GOPPUS

• • • • • • • • • • • • • • • • •

14   UDD BVFR QYDQSY YHQYPU

CDFWYZK AZDB WYBDPZVPR, CTYF UTY

BDKU CDFWYZAXS UTGFJ DA VSS GK

NXKU TVOGFJ GU.   —CVSUYZ CGFPTYSS

• • • • • • • • • • • • • • • • •

15   P MKZKAVUJI UY YHLKHQK CSH

CHVRY SPVF PZZ SUY ZUWK JH AKMHLK

CKZZ-RQHCQ, PQF JSKQ CKPVY FPVR

DZPYYKY JH PBHUF AKUQD VKMHDQUEKF.

            —WVKF PZZKQ

16   BOT AGP BU FGBFO G
WRCFWSTHGSS KN BU AGKB CRBKS BOT
HGSS NBUEN MUSSKRD GRJ BOTR EKFW
KB CE.   —HUH CTFWTM

• • • • • • • • • • • • • • • • • •

17   ADQNQ INQ AMF TPJEBAJ PF DEVIP
GQTPU MTBB QPSENQ: ADIA DQ DIJ PF
JQPJQ FX DEVFN, IPS ADIA DQ DIJ
PQHQN OPFMP ANFEGBQ.

                         —JTPLBITN BQMTJ

• • • • • • • • • • • • • • • • • •

18   C'SP ISPJ-PEWOGKPE ARNPYT CH
GYY KVP KVCHDN C NVIWYEH'K VGSP
BHIQH GK GYY.   —HIPY OIQGJE

19   OD DMMX ET QOQDTTV FTKAY DM
ZOYPMGTA O RKZ VM DKBTVD QMA
SAODOVL, UWD O PMWBZV'D LOGT OD
WN UTPKWYT UF DRKD DOET O SKY DMM
QKEMWY.   —AMUTAD UTVPRBTF

• • • • • • • • • • • • • • • • •

20   ZLN IDZ WV QGTDSSLGACVQ GJ ZLN
JDGE, WNC ZLN DPV QLLIVQ GJ ZLN
QLA'C CPZ.   —WVYVPEZ TGEET

• • • • • • • • • • • • • • • • •

21   VWG SPQJ VWKPZ K EGZEGV
YNSMV IJ CYTV KT VWG QGPZVW SH KV.
KH K WYU VS QKFG IJ QKHG YZYKP, K'U
IYOG VWG TYIG IKTVYOGT, SPQJ TSSPGE.
                    —VYQQMQYW NYPOWGYU

22   X QSXOJSXO JBSJ JBP ZBCSVP
"S FKON ZKPQ" XV VXQZFI S
HKOJCSGXHJXKO XO JPCQV.

—PGNSC SFFSO ZKP

• • • • • • • • • • • • • • • • •

23   CKMCQK QKXEU PMNKRVAUH KFKES
TXS, XUT X QMR MB RANKP AR'P RVXR
DVXR RVKS QKXEUKT RVK TXS JKBMEK DXP
DEMUH.   —JAQQ FXLHVXU

• • • • • • • • • • • • • • • • •

24   DJ'BJ AWX LONUVKJ-XIDP JUIPIQNUF
NP LAJ UIGPLOH ZIO HJWOF PID, WPX
QIFL IZ GF WOJP'L JBJP XWQC HJL.

—QIKKH NBNPF

25   AV KVS SCI PVFS PVUDKY PVPIKSF
VM VTG BDUIF MDKA TF JBB RDSCVTS
RVGAF?   —PJGZIB PJGZIJT

∙ ∙ ∙ ∙ ∙ ∙ ∙ ∙ ∙ ∙ ∙ ∙ ∙ ∙ ∙ ∙ ∙ ∙

26   LQRRNI MBI QE DOI MGSGMCR
HICQKR GOIZ XMDOIC DQLI EDMCDE
TMDTOQZB VH GQDO LKDOIC ZMDVCI.

                          —OMCKNR TKXXQZ

∙ ∙ ∙ ∙ ∙ ∙ ∙ ∙ ∙ ∙ ∙ ∙ ∙ ∙ ∙ ∙ ∙

27   KCIISAK YSDNFBCY MXGI TCBQXGC
ENX YNA'I RNDC Q LQA SG QRLNGI QG
GSRRE QG KCIISAK LQFFSCY MXGI
TCBQXGC ENX YN.   —UGQ UGQ KQTNF

28   ILJLD YLIB ZEETR, NED IE EIL LJLD

DLPXDIR PGLA; PGL EIYM ZEETR F GVJL FI

AM YFZDVDM VDL ZEETR PGVP EPGLD

NEYT GVJL YLIP AL.

—VIVPEYL NDVIKL

● ● ● ● ● ● ● ● ● ● ● ● ● ● ● ● ●

29   EJS EWFAHRS VQEJ SPANRQEG QD

EJNE VS FORG TSDQWS QE VQEJ FAW

DABSWQFWD.   —JSOWG HSKPAS

● ● ● ● ● ● ● ● ● ● ● ● ● ● ● ●

30   O WEC'U UQOCJ EK XHH UQL

ZORLAS DPU EK XHH UQL DLXPUS UQXU

RUOHH ALZXOCR.   —XCCL KAXCJ

31   EDKXK FXK EMY EDHROI EDFE MHTT
VK VKTHKZKC YL FRU SFR MDFEIYKZKX,
FRC YRK YL EDKS HI EDFE DK DFI EFJKR EY
CXHRJ.   —VYYED EFXJHROEYR

• • • • • • • • • • • • • • • • • •

32   Q HDMDPQUJQT JR RWFDYWKX NBW
NWT'P DQP QTXPBJTM PBQP ZQT BQHD
ZBJEKUDT.   —KQHJK YUDTTDU

• • • • • • • • • • • • • • • • •

33   XHS BVG DNFC V DNYCRNLC VGK,
VR RPC CGK HY NR, IGHO LHQC VZHSR
HRPCQ JCHJDC RPVG XHS IGHO VZHSR
XHSQWCDY.   —ZCQXD LVQIPVL

34   GCHNT KDVTFQ NSD JGD MTWR
ESDNJCSDQ MT DNSJG JGNJ NWWMU
JGDVS EGVWOSDT JM EMHD KNEP
GMHD.   —KVWW EMQKR

• • • • • • • • • • • • • • • • •

35   W VJMJU RQIYX IVXJUTOBVX GQA
OAQ FJV RBV AUWOJ B SQQL OQEJOGJU;
OQ FJ OGBO'T YWLJ OGUJJ ZJQZYJ
EJOOWVE OQEJOGJU OQ GBMJ B SBSD.
                        —JMJYDV ABIEG

• • • • • • • • • • • • • • • • •

36   BRK BDSFVMK YCBR MCPK CI BRK
PJAB MJIK CA BRJB XSF OKB BS BRK
SBRKD KIN CI JI JYPFM RFDDX.
                        —USRI UKIAKI

37   VDU ZVUCD'Q ZHCKVBUY DUG
MEDZC GHQFVTQ KVDCUDQHDX QV
MVCU CHXFQ VJ QFU CFVYU JVY E
BUYA MVDX QHSU.   —EDZYU XHZU

• • • • • • • • • • • • • • • • •

38   T RLBXD VP QMVHVIEMR BRBTKKD
NQFQTKR LGTL LGQ AQRL LEIQ LV ABD
THDLGEHY ER KTRL DQTN.

                              —ITNLD TKKQH

• • • • • • • • • • • • • • • • •

39   CXZ'W CQZY WJGIJDLIY JB X
ZIH QYIX ZIKIG UBIW PXDT JB QJW
BGQUQZXE YQCIZWQBZW.

                    —BEQKIG HIZYIEE LBECIW

40   OQ CGW TFDYOV YOPWR ISF,
ISF'BW LSSH. RGZPWRTWZBW AZR Z
VSKKSM, HSAM-CS-WZBCG ABOCWB
OM GOR HZI.   —KOVPWI RTOYYZMW

• • • • • • • • • • • • • • • • •

41   KXEY XF YIFXYU MJIP THB'Q MJXPS;
IKK MJIM XF PYZYFFIUT XF MH IZZYGM
MJY XAGHFFXDKY, QH CXMJHBM MJY
XPQXFGYPFIDKY, IPQ DYIU MJY
XPMHKYUIDKY.   —SIMJKYYP PHUUXF

• • • • • • • • • • • • • • • • •

42   O YG PBMV Y FJUMOZ
KBAKNAYOBKN RQP QYW JBCKNWAPPC
QOW AOGK.   —FYUMP FOZYWWP

43   ZFKLLKX ML CWK EQT JWR, WQUMTY
TRCWMTY CR LQD, QZLCQMTL AGRE
YMUMTY JRGXD KUMXKTOK RA CWK
AQOC.   —YKRGYK KFMRC

• • • • • • • • • • • • • • • • •

44   OZHUFUWD UD RZF S ISE
OLZMJDDUZR. UM XZP DPWWJJE FKJLJ
SLJ TSRX LJVSLED; UM XZP EUDNLSWJ
XZPLDJHM XZP WSR SHVSXD VLUFJ S
IZZG.   —LZRSHE LJSNSR

• • • • • • • • • • • • • • • • •

45   CNU YZAGC ZV SAJAGF, QGW ZV
IUAGF QG ZYCAPAEC, AE CZ IU VZZSAEN
UGZDFN CZ IUSAUJU CNU IUEC AE BUC
CZ HZPU.   —YUCUL DECAGZJ

46   BKSMSBUTM LOYINW WIRQIC, LOU
YU BSX LT URMX NRQX QYUK YXBMTNYLIT
WQYHUXTWW.   —HSYUK LSINQYX

• • • • • • • • • • • • • • • • •

47   ZHSZTAZDPZ AU DMJ OQKJ
QKSSZDU JM VMF; AJ AU OQKJ VMF WM
OAJQ OQKJ QKSSZDU JM VMF.

                    —KEWMFU QFHEZV

• • • • • • • • • • • • • • • • •

48   FTN NSDYNDF USG FH IHWLYWIN
ZG JYXD FTSF FTNG XHW'F QNSPPG
WNNX DHZNFTYWE YD FH ENF YF OHQ
FTNZ.   —MHSW IHPPYWD

49   NII R QWWO AK JNHW N PKJWOU
RM N DNZH, N DKIRPWJNQ, NQO N
DZWAAU SRZI.   —PYNZIRW PYNDIRQ

• • • • • • • • • • • • • • • • • •

50   S ASY EZDWYO INPPWYD MWO
GWOBUA PZZPM PMZ CWQOP PWAZ MZ
EWPZO UCC AUQZ PMSY MZ ISY IMZG.

—MZQE ISZY

• • • • • • • • • • • • • • • • • •

51   AZCINEWQQH, L XBLEO LJ W
UNVWE BWIE'X VZX XBZ CLYBX VWE GH
XBZ XLVZ IBZ'I XUZEXH-JNRC, IBZ VWH
GZ QRPOH.   —SZGNCWB OZCC

52   P LJQH DR ARKY PE N BPKQ
ZIHKNED BNMDRKI. IRL MRLFHE'D XNKY
NEIAZQKQ EQNK DZQ XFNMQ.

—JDQCQE AKPWZD

· · · · · · · · · · · · · · · · · · ·

53   QENUN YUN QIK IYCZ KD
ZGUNYBTSF OTFEQ: QK VN QEN PYSBON
KU QEN WTUUKU QEYQ UNDONPQZ TQ.

—NBTQE IEYUQKS

· · · · · · · · · · · · · · · · · ·

54   C QXZI HJ JXKIXOI YLX UIZJHJMJ HO
LXDGHOR LHJ XYO PHIYJ CTMIZ YI LCPI
IODHRLMIOIG LHK YHML XWZJ.

—KCDFXDK TXZQIJ

55   PML POCIAKL RBPM PML QOCHBP
DJDPLX MYD YKRYJD ALLG PMYP BP BD
MBFMKJ IGQOCHBPYAKL PC XCDP
QLCQKL.   —L.A. RMBPL

• • • • • • • • • • • • • • • • • •

56   SYM SD ROM SNAMGR OJZLY
YMMAG KG OLPKYF GSZMSYM RS
ISYAMW IOMWM HSJ LWM IOMY HSJ
ASY'R ESZM OSZM LR YKFOR.

                    —ZLWFLWMR ZMLA

• • • • • • • • • • • • • • • • • •

57   DEJ ZOWA DEQOV DEUD GUYJG HG
SKZF DEJ PHKJUHMKUMA QG QDG
QOJSSQMQJOMA.   —JHVJOJ FMMUKDEA

58   UZ TDNXQH LOQR NJ ODZ NXDN
WN YDO YWIAQR NJ FJ TWOXWMF JM
OLMRDZ. ELN XQ MQBQH ODWR
DMZNXWMF DEJLN RHDY SJAQH.

—FHJBQH IPQBQPDMR

• • • • • • • • • • • • • • • • •

59   HDI BZM QIXVF Z CTLDMN RXCT
QZHDMNCU, QIC HDI BZM'C UXC DM
XC JDL VDME.   —QDLXU HNVCUXM

• • • • • • • • • • • • • • • • •

60   BKOC PKKTB ZMC JK PC JZBJCX,
KJGCMB JK PC BIZYYKICX, ZLX BKOC
NCI JK PC HGCICX ZLX XAQCBJCX.

—NMZLHAB PZHKL

61   NRQDUHT MY AMLUS FXBKIQDU
TXMLKI QDRKBOD HXRH YDC NDMNKD
CBKK YBUI HXDBQ FXBKIQDU RT
DUFXRUHBUS RT HXDA IM.

—VRQVRQR CRKHDQT

• • • • • • • • • • • • • • • • • •

62   OFMDG MTMIGW SDJM SM UYEMG
DIV BDCS; EG EW HICZ GFEKCMW GQDG
EFFEGDGM SZ IMFTMW.

—UYMMI TEBGHFED

• • • • • • • • • • • • • • • • • •

63   DV ODZ WRPPZS JZTFKYV ZSDVTM
UVMSTZIM SDV ATKUFV ZYVT ODKWD DV
DKHMVXJ HEMS BRMM.

—FVZTFV DVTAVTS

64   NAQ DMH BE ABCH HYHWGLUBIM

HAEH. LN SDCH D EZVVHEE NJ BL,

GNZ'YH MNL LN ELDWL GNZIM.

—JWHQ DELDBWH

• • • • • • • • • • • • • • • • •

65   QYQRHZ YFH YEXYDZ VBFH

NFBPQEH NKYO DBP NKBPUKN—YOS

VBFH XBOSHFJPE.   —LKYFEHZ BZUBBS

• • • • • • • • • • • • • • • •

66   XLI JB RM XLI CJCIO DJRB "GRU DJKI.

KJDX FIIT." FLP JBYIOXRDI? R JKOIJBP

VRDDIB RX. XLIP'OI EHDX OHGGRMU RX

RM.   —PJTZY DVROMZAA

67   HP RUMT YHPFUAP TISHKR PFIP SUA
TFUACE KMNMD FINM QUDM OFHCEDMK
PFIK SUA FINM OID YHKEUYT.

—MDQI LUQLMOX

• • • • • • • • • • • • • • • • • •

68   HAUHTA SKU SUWO IVEEVRQ XUSR
QAE HJVX DUWA EKJR HAUHTA SKU
SUWO IEJRXVRQ YH.   —UQXAR RJIK

• • • • • • • • • • • • • • • • • •

69   JA TPMX TPD LTZMS QUKD NVT
MJKDE: NQD AJOEN JP VQJLQ NT HUID
TPD'E HJENUIDE, UPS NQD EDLTPS JP
VQJLQ NT WOTAJN YX NQDH.

—S.Q. MUVODPLD

70   CVHK NHJNOH RHHN ZHOODKF EJW

ZVYZ EJW IYK'Z QJ Y ZVDKF, EJW RDKQ

JB ODRH ZJ ZAE DZ.

—LYAFYAHZ IVYGH GLDZV

• • • • • • • • • • • • • • • • •

71   MKDSLQTFXQ KVVUKCD FX AU

PLYYUR MLFS FMX OLQRD XP

VXYLFLELKQD— FSXDU FCGLQT FX TUF KQ

LQZUDFLTKFLXQ DFKCFUR, KQR FSXDU

FCGLQT FX TUF XQU DFXVVUR.

—UKCY MLYDXQ

• • • • • • • • • • • • • • • • •

72   ADZ'F UH MCVUBH. QDC'TH ZDF

FMJF ITHJF.   —IDBAJ VHST

73   AGR UKORMNDCYZ GYCL DW
BDIRMCKRCA HYC CRIRM MROZYHR AGR
GRZOUCB GYCL DW Y CRUBGTDM.

—GSTRMA G. GSKOGMRP

• • • • • • • • • • • • • • • • • •

74   FJBIWKG AC T CAGSG FRJBIMR
ERAQR EG CAXF BIJ TQLITAPFTPQGC.
FRBCG FBB WAM FB ZTCC FRJBIMR TJG
BIJ XJAGPHC.   —TJKGPG XJTPQAC

• • • • • • • • • • • • • • • • • •

75   JQVE UVFF YDBCVX JQD FCXW NH
JQD HYDD NXFZ EN FNXO CE VJ VE JQD
QNBD NH JQD PYCLD.   —DFBDY WCLVE

76 MJ ZAX EYL QIID ZAXU PIYC NPIL

YVV YTAXH ZAX YUI VAOMLF HPIMUO,

MH'O BXOH DAOOMTVI ZAX PYKIL'H

FUYODIC HPI OMHXYHMAL. —BIYL QIUU

• • • • • • • • • • • • • • • • •

77 UYO HODXHQXNPO UYSJV XNFKU

GYXQOGBOXHO SG UYXU YO HOXPPR

SG TOHR VFFZ, SJ GBSUO FI XPP UYO

BOFBPO EYF GXR YO SG TOHR VFFZ.

—HFNOHU VHXTOG

• • • • • • • • • • • • • • • • •

78 M UMK'H DRO OR OMPL M IRO RY

SQKZHGULKO OR BJZOL M JLMIIC YQKKC

XRRP. —LJKLHO GLUZKDBMC

79   TES VLJ RLDFNT HSQWR UBR
VBLALVURA EG L XLJ MT BEY BR UARLUD
UBEDR YBE VLJ QE JEUBFJW GEA BFX.

—HLXRD Q. XFNRD

• • • • • • • • • • • • • • • •

80   Z VJMO MOQOEZHZGD. Z VJMO ZM
JH LNIV JH TOJDNMH. FNM Z IJD'M HMGT
OJMZDX TOJDNMH.   —GAHGD YOQQOH

• • • • • • • • • • • • • • • •

81   PVQ TQDP CFE XADP TQCJPBYJS
PVBFLD BF PVQ RAZSE UCFFAP TQ DQQF
AZ QWQF PAJUVQE. PVQH XJDP TQ YQSP
RBPV PVQ VQCZP.   —VQSQF GQSSQZ

82   NWG RO AXEAIMISKI OE FBJW FEXQ

OBJJQOOTBV NWQS RD ODRXO BA

WIDXQK DWIS NWQS RD DXRQO DE

ODRX BA TXRQSKVG TQQVRSM?

—PQXDXISK XBOOQVV

• • • • • • • • • • • • • • • • •

83   WPR IJU TE EYIWWROX JA WT

ATTWPR IVN RVFTSOIKR SA QX IAASOJVK

SA TE WPR WOSWP TE IV TZJVJTV CR PIBR

IYORINX ETOURN IQTSW TSOARYBRA.

—RNJWP AJWCRYY

• • • • • • • • • • • • • • • • •

84   IXLJRIY VXB MZRLW, RG VXB JXOW LX

PW CIV YXXU, MRKK WNWZ QXDW XBL

CA VXB GRZAL JXOWU.

—KRKKRCI JWKKDCI

85   B THSD UFCPN WTHW WTD RDEW
QHM WF ABSD HNSBZD WF MFCL
ZTBONLDP BE WF UBPN FCW QTHW
WTDM QHPW, HPN WTDP HNSBED WTDI
WF NF BW.   —THLLM WLCIHP

• • • • • • • • • • • • • • • • • •

86   FAUKR FAUJ DIYIZJ JLI JLWAPLJU ZQH
KQUYKDZJKWQU WX JLI YIWYNI ZQH JLI
JKFIU.   —PIWDPI PIDULVKQ

• • • • • • • • • • • • • • • • • •

87   EPRTEJ-ZWOD UWOD DWWB
QRDFSLR VRTRDKIIJ DRZRDQ EW EUR
IRTVEU WZ ESBR EUKE SE EKYRQ ZWD
EUR LIOG QKTAPSLU EW KDDSFR.

                    —ZDKT IRGWPSEH

88   WCDT NLVTP BUD YX PKLVI UDT
XUPM IL POXUW, YHI IKXCV XBKLXP UVX
IVHAM XDTAXPP.   —RLIKXV IXVXPU

● ● ● ● ● ● ● ● ● ● ● ● ● ● ● ● ●

89   ISYFY NE OM SKHGO RFMPZYH
USNXS XMKZT OMI PY EMZCYT NV
RYMRZY UMKZT ENHRZQ TM GE N
GTCNEY.   —DMFY CNTGZ

● ● ● ● ● ● ● ● ● ● ● ● ● ● ● ●

90   YZ KJP NDDE JC GRKYCX SIYCXG
RVD XJYCX SJ QD QRB, KJP IRAD R XJJB
UIRCUD JZ QDYCX R EVJEIDS.

                    —YGRRU QRGIDAYG GYCXDV

91   XAUWQEXYC ENAAJYQEXLU
LGWNJRG DJLLNYC, L-CGQWLC, XYF
DJAVUW CLQEZUWC LGU OXP CNAU
EJILJWUC JCU FWJAC.

—LQA AEEXWLGP

• • • • • • • • • • • • • • • • •

92   YGN WAZK XR FMZMKACN
MQAOGYC XSQD EFXS YGN GMSK
YGMY KXNC SXY OZMCF.

—PXGS WNZZD

• • • • • • • • • • • • • • • • •

93   NMLRID DRK SFRQ QFLK ILRT, EXQ
QFLK NJT'Q DRK VQ VT NRKQVIL
BRTAXRAL.   —ARVB AJNSVT

94   H KPLLKO AOQOKKPRJ JRZ HJU LTOJ
PW H BRRU LTPJB, HJU HW JOSOWWHAD
PJ LTO VRKPLPSHK ZRAKU HW WLRAGW PJ
LTO VTDWPSHK.

—LTRGHW YOMMOAWRJ

• • • • • • • • • • • • • • • • • •

95   M GWD'X URNMRPR MD QD
QCXRLNMCR, QNXFWZOF M QH
ULMDOMDO Q KFQDOR WC ZDGRLARQL.

—AWWGS QNNRD

• • • • • • • • • • • • • • • • • •

96   JR K ZJMFDZ DR DCCDQEGMJEX
KCCWKQB, FDM'E CGYY FDZM ELW
BLKFW.   —EDV CWEWQB

97   RCRXW TRYRXVFMLY DVGTPN VF FPR
LDQ BVNPMLYN, SGF XRDMTMLGNDW
BLDDLON FPR YRO.

—PRYXW QVCMQ FPLXRVG

• • • • • • • • • • • • • • • • •

98   QKWSW UA JZ HWJXUJR QKW NFVQ
QKFQ TSUQWSA AKZOMH GW SWFH
GOQ JZQ AWWJ. SFSWMX FSW QKWX F
TUJAZCW AURKQ.   —WHJF NWSGWS

• • • • • • • • • • • • • • • • •

99   H RIYGBS JU LIY H ABSUIL YI DBHL IL
VCY H ABSUIL YI RHWB DBHLJLQ
CLLBFBUUHSX.

—EISIYGX FHLPJBDE PJUGBS

100 YK X IFA ELNOT FMZF VFLJ DXO, YZ YT WGSXLTG QG YT KFMI FK VFL; WLZ YK X SXZ IFGT ZQG TXNG ZQYMA, YZ YT WGSXLTG VFLJ DXO YT PXJNGJ.

—X.M. PQYZGQGXI

• • • • • • • • • • • • • • • • •

101 FUT WNP XES DU FUTG ZERS UG FUTG HUKK, HTD FUT WNPPUD XES DU FUTG DFLSZGEDSG. KUUPSG UG XNDSG FUT VTKD GSISNX FUTG DGTS KSXR EP FUTG LNJSK. —XSUP TGEK

• • • • • • • • • • • • • • • • •

102 EPQCLSI QX UWI RMAYQVIAU UWPU KQOIX XLRRIXX QUX ECPOMS.

—USLVPA RPHMUI

103   HOF ZNRH DFEIHYSIM HOYUJR YU

HOF CNQMK EQF HOF ZNRH IRFMFRR:

XFETNTWR EUK MYMYFR, SNQ YURHEUTF.

—LNOU QIRWYU

• • • • • • • • • • • • • • • • •

104   TG GCZKL C JESD GTBK GE XKCJ C

IVEZKS XKCVG. IHG QJCMTSD ESK EN BM

CJIHBL YCS XKJQ.   —NVCSZ LTSCGVC

• • • • • • • • • • • • • • • • •

105   OEE VBABEBYODBUM ZON SJUI DBIC

DU DBIC RCVUIC O DZBM VJTND UACJ O

AUEVOMU US JCAUETDBUM.

—ZOACEUVH CEEBN

106   HSJ MRTOA KV CJXRTJ DRN, GIA
DRN IJJA IRH HGWJ KH RT OJGPJ KH GV
KH MGV MSJI DRN QGYJ KI.

—BGYJV CGOAMKI

• • • • • • • • • • • • • • • • •

107   VSWU PUW BTCB ISTI T VDEIWD EB
QTBSEPUTKRW PUW HDTJIEJTRRC TRVTCB
NWTUB ISTI SW EB TFNEDWF KC
HWPHRW XUFWD ISEDIC.

—MWPDMW PDVWRR

• • • • • • • • • • • • • • • • •

108   DSESAT KY D YPDYHT XHGGHCPV
KAAPVKDEPGQ LQ GHHOKTF XHZCDZV EH
YRZKTF.   —VHSF GDZYHT

109   YNH TZBN NQIH Q FQRRZUJ XUT.
MQTKQZJR QR GZIHGD QR ZY ZR
FUZJYGHRR.   —XTQJBUZRH RQKQJ

• • • • • • • • • • • • • • • • •

110   HXX ZLS HCJXUCUM HLU IRXREFNHX.
CJUT MZUHV UEFXRMJ HEB ZLSQHERCT.

                              —FSLBRU JSKU

• • • • • • • • • • • • • • • • •

111   OZXMAOE AQ UZYJ HALLAWPVX,
SOH XMJYJLZYJ UZYJ GYJWAZPQ, XMSO
XZ DJ SDVJ XZ HJWAHJ.   —OSGZVJZO

112   SK SH G WGAJIW BNNM ASJW
SJWIIW KVGK LGJ'K KVSJU NZ GK EIGHK
KTN TGFH NZ HBIEESJQ GJF TNMW.

—GJWMIT RGLUHNJ

• • • • • • • • • • • • • • • • •

113   XDEVLZVE XQV X YIIM ALNBJVLZV AL
BITV XLM GVBO UVVO AH DQAYGH XLM
MVBAZXHV.

—QIDVQH BIJAE EHVTVLEIL

• • • • • • • • • • • • • • • • •

114   AWMFPCGV KD CPG DPUVCGDC
XKDCWQRG ZGCIGGQ CIU TGUTAG.

—NKRCUV ZUVFG

115 Z WZQ ODGHDR HJ SHPD WZPHFN Z
IZPD RHXV ZSS XVD WDJX HFNODQHDFXJ
ZFQ VZGHFN JMLDMFD JHX MF HX.

—QZFHDSSD JXDDS

• • • • • • • • • • • • • • • • • •

116 JVX DXEJ GLHP LE VX CVZ BHOXE JVX
EBHGGXEJ HBZTQJ ZR GFLQW WZ JVX
GZQWXEJ CHF.   —EHBTXG DTJGXP

• • • • • • • • • • • • • • • • • •

117 W ARHZE VSALPSG WF WEJZU YRSF
RS TSWZHOSG URWU RS RWG W THKRU
FLU LFZQ UL VS THKRU VJU WZGL UL VS
YTLFK.   —URLPWG GOWGO

118   SZKMKSQTM SGARHRQR GE PZKQ
LGV CG GA QZT QZHMC KAC EGVMQZ
QMHTR.   —NKUTR UHSZTATM

• • • • • • • • • • • • • • • • •

119   TXKFRR LZT YEZZRF NZ CZ WJFHN
NEGXWR VGNE GN, GN UHQFR XZ
CGSSFJFXYF EZV UTYE MZVFJ LZT EHPF.
                                   —ZMJHE VGXSJFL

• • • • • • • • • • • • • • • • •

120   NZ'W OXZ G UXXJ NJQG ZX ZMV ZX
LFZ VXFM DNYQ NOZX G OXSQR ... OXZ
VXFM RGZQWZ DNYQ GOVDGV.
                                   —OXMBGO BGNRQM

121   XNO VPCJOL SVO HFAX FJSPX XNO
VODE COBQF QE XNFX XNOG YSKO
HQWNXE. DNOV GSP WQKO XNOC
ASVHLSVXFXQSVE GSP WOX FXXOVXQSV.

—VODX WQVWLQAN

• • • • • • • • • • • • • • • • • •

122   BTRVXIN XR Z KZIWXLN VWZV,
DWNL RPKNPLN WZR PLIN QXUNL XV
VWN RVZGVXLQ YTRW, GPCCR PL PM
XVRNCM.   —BPWL QZCRDPGVWA

• • • • • • • • • • • • • • • • • •

123   DBQ WYQFDQID WXXP ZXK TFM PX
GXY FMXDBQY HI MXD NKID DX IBFYQ
ZXKY YHTBQI AKD DX YQCQFO DX BHS
BHI XEM.   —AQMNFSHM PHIYFQOH

124 JCVS IGX UBD LGT ZVTLVRNBGS, IGX
FBWRGHVT BN'W U DGHBSA NUTAVN.

—AVGTAV LBWCVT

• • • • • • • • • • • • • • • •

125 GSIIXZJEE XE FXWJ S YVBBJQAFL
KGXNG SIIJSQE SZP PJFXRGBE VE ADQ
DZJ YQXJA UDUJZB, YVB EDDZ AFXBE
SKSL. —SZZS ISMFDMS

• • • • • • • • • • • • • • • •

126 QAYRS SDE QHDYAXH GUJ MXUDC
UAX GUXRNUEY DXH. QZ QREC JDEIY IU
YHH IU REBRERIZ. —YIHFRH JUECHX

127   UQ OG HZZIC AWP HRRS WSG
XZJCR U XZFDP SZM AWTR HRRS USTUMRP
MZ AZDDGXZZP, WSP UQ MARG AWP
HRRS WSG HRMMRJ U XZFDP SZM AWTR
EZOR.   —JWGOZSP EAWSPDRJ

• • • • • • • • • • • • • • • • •

128   EUWOOTQL CG WUU QCAYO—CE
LMJ SMD'O CDYWUT.

                         —WSUWC GOTRTDGMD

• • • • • • • • • • • • • • • • •

129   NGZSTFTA NHQTL KH SGTV QCXS KH
SNBET ZX NTYY ZX QTL SH RT SGHCIGS
GZYJ ZX IHHK. YCEUBYV, SGBX BX LHS
KBJJBECYS.   —EGZAYHSST NGBSSHL

130   LNU GFJXXYNXYGJIV IN TJPP ILGE
XPJFVI VJYIL ULVF TPVJYPH GI GE NTVJF.

—JYILRY T. TPJYZV

• • • • • • • • • • • • • • • • •

131   QEY WBXF QESBT QEUQ VQWDV
TWO HJWN VYBOSBT UBWQEYJ HXWWO
SV QEUQ QEY HSJVQ WBY CUV GVYXYVV.

—BSKEWXUV KEUNHWJQ

• • • • • • • • • • • • • • • • •

132   BZD LYE GOWLZRUT VZTU YSZDQ Y
XUTWZE OE YE NZDT ZC XJYB QNYE OE Y
BUYT ZC LZERUTWYQOZE.   —XJYQZ

133   IUDF'C AMH J LJIRUGK CEJNBL, J
WBBQ WIJTFQ HEJH CHQMHC JGN
DQFHC EUC EBMQ MWBG HEF CHJKF,
JGN HEFG UC EFJQN GB YBQF.

—LUIIUJY CEJRFCWFJQF

● ● ● ● ● ● ● ● ● ● ● ● ● ● ● ● ●

134   CNBUM BD MZP IQBWP SP IJX
SBUUBTCUX HLQ KLBTC SZJM SP JQP
CLBTC ML KL JTXSJX.

—BDJEPUUP ZLUUJTK

● ● ● ● ● ● ● ● ● ● ● ● ● ● ● ● ●

135   R JRCKX JF FNK AOTIRB'M NKJYF,
JGX TD JBBRXKGF R NRF RF RG FNK
MFHCJBN.   —OAFHG MRGBIJRY

136   VFY ZESZHPY GDK Z JDDA LFDRWE
JY ZV WYZLV ZL IRPF ZL VFY PDLV DG VFY
WRHPF ZV QFCPF CV QZL ECLPRLLYE.

—PZWSCH VKCWWCH

• • • • • • • • • • • • • • • • •

137   RY R UKMJ "DRBMJAJGGK," EFJ
KSMRJBDJ CNSGM QJ GNNZRBH NSE
YNA K QNMV RB EFJ DNKDF.

—KGYAJM FREDFDNDZ

• • • • • • • • • • • • • • • • •

138   TIVNBQNPXY, KXCI TPUQXOW,
NPBGKA DILXV UO PBSI; DGO, GVKXCI
TPUQXOW, XO NPBGKA IVA OPIQI.

—TKUQI DBBOPI KGTI

139   ZJYTBSG, VUTW JS YTPJWX SE SCFT

BEES, JX C OZCWS EA BCOJI PBEVSU.

—PTEBPT VCXUJWPSEW

• • • • • • • • • • • • • • • • •

140   ZX VBP CORU CBMJ CKGG LBRK,

EKGKTU O DPEV NOR; UIK BUIKM JZRL

IOE RB UZNK.   —KGDKMU IPDDOML

• • • • • • • • • • • • • • • • •

141   GBUBT VGKYHQ WG WHHVJWQNT

YGQVH WOQBT INY RWUB XTNKKBP QRB

TVUBT.   —XNTPBHH RYHH

142   ZOCTS SQB HCXS CUEFEJZNESL
SQZS ZJL MUESBU DZJ QCIB SC ZDQEBPB
QCJBXSNL EX SC XSBZN MESQ FCCY
RTYFHBJS.   —RCXQ OENNEJFX

• • • • • • • • • • • • • • • • • •

143   FPZA ZD ZHAPCJ WGYQO AC FJGAQ
NCOA GO PGO OGBDZAHJQ CD APQ
XZTY CU Z TPQTY.   —XJQDIZD UJZDTGO

• • • • • • • • • • • • • • • • • •

144   N PGWCP VJSICGS N ZYT SC HSNDK
CD VJZZ TYS NPCGDK HCWY CSIYP VNA.
                      —QCID SGKCP

145 RDHTL LHXDT LZZM CNPDSHNJ HA
JHFD RDHTL NAAHLTDM PZ RNFD N YNFD
NTM UNXHTL PUD RNPPDS CNMD WZS
GZQ. —SZANJHTM SQAADJJ

• • • • • • • • • • • • • • • •

146 KMS'Y DMSKGFDGSK YM ESFXHIIGK
IZUMB. YBQ HY VMB JZIV Z KZQ VHBFY.
—UBMMXF ZYXHSFMS

• • • • • • • • • • • • • • • •

147 PA MFQ XEHPR PAIEHMJN B ZQVQAI
PH EHEBZZN AL XLJQ MFBA HLXQLAQ
DPMF MDL RLAHQREMPCQ FPM HPAVZQH.
—VBJJN MJEIQBE

148   NVCM BVKW ILWT SLWJ'FW

BZDDWN; BZSM SZYW Z KWMMZCW

ZTN CWS XZBY SV JVQ.   —KZFJ XDJ

• • • • • • • • • • • • • • • • •

149   JBOXGZVET VR G IQENQJRRVHJ

BVRXEHJQU EC EOQ EPT VNTEQGTXJ.

—PVMM BOQGTZ

• • • • • • • • • • • • • • • • •

150   XA PCOR GTCI OSQ SYQ

TVVCHRQGTQA GDR PTVMRI MS KS

GSXRUZTFR GDR'I VRHRQ JRRV JROSQR.

C GTCI, "DSP 'JSYM MDR NCMFDRV?"

—QSIVRA ITVKRQOCRZI

151   KQENGUX WNZRV GNVIMRVQEQKQUX.

UBZU QV HBX WMVU WNR AGNZA QU.

—JNMGJN ENGRZGA VBZH

• • • • • • • • • • • • • • • •

152   XDR JRLGFI TJLIBULJRIXG LIB

TJLIBVDAWBJRI TRX LWFIT GF PRWW

AG XDLX XDRZ DLYR L VFOOFI RIROZ.

—GLO WRYRIGFI

(handwritten overlay: THE REASON GRANDPARENTS AND GRANDCHILDREN GET ALONG SO WELL IS THAT THEY HAVE A COMMON ENEMY. SAM LECENSON. f=1,9~ A=)

• • • • • • • • • • • • • • • •

153   KGZMCU SKL QPMSMQO WPGMOL

INH MO XMJL KGZMCU SKL KGCUFGC

OGI INH'ZL UNS G WPLSSI CLQJ.

—LXM AGXXGQK

154   U AZQYK RMVDQCM DZ FQMBB
DIOD OVZV, AIZ ACZDM BZ GOVX JZMGB
AUDIZQD BUFVUVF DIMG, AOB ZLDMV O
AZGOV.   —RUCFUVUO AZZYL

• • • • • • • • • • • • • • • • •

155   HGKQWCWJ K DKT ZJKSB XNJ, GW
ZJKSB XNJ K DOJKFEW. WCWJS ZJKSWJ
JWUPFWB OQBWEX QN QGOB: "LJWKQ
LNU, LJKTQ QGKQ QHOFW QHN AW TNQ
XNPJ."   —OCKT QPJLWTWC

• • • • • • • • • • • • • • • • •

156   PCUQ KL RYTUH LY EYSUKFQ EYYJ,
LCU XUHH IGLCUQLKR LCU MULLUS.
                    —FUSIXJ QIRCTIQ

157 IZLOTPQFZC FC QOIHOT FB PMVPXB

P UFTQEO, GEQ IZLOTPQFZC FC

HTFCJFHMO FB PMVPXB P UFJO.

—QKZIPB HPFCO

• • • • • • • • • • • • • • • • •

158 APJI ISTWRHZN OZ LN QTI IPJI

OTGLZ NIJSN SWQ CTS TCCLVZ, RWI

IPJI IPZE CLQX LI ZJNE IT BZI ZHZVIZX.

—NPJQJ JHZKJQXZS

• • • • • • • • • • • • • • • • •

159 SY SL YEI ZGWGFD CU CRB GXI

YEGY YEI DCRHX GBI LC NRLD YIGKESHX

RL YEGY YEID EGPI HC YSZI WIUY YC

WIGBH.   —IBSK ECUUIB

160   JEK TGBRI OBR TOYKI OFK OPTOMI

QB JEK IGRK QH JEK OUPKIJ

BOYGWOJQFI.   —KRTOFR WGUUQB

• • • • • • • • • • • • • • • • •

161   Z MNNX NCVDQ QN MI ZB SOI

FSOX QN MLIZX CF QDI JLNGIB HIZ

RSQDSB CH.   —JLZBG XZJXZ

• • • • • • • • • • • • • • • • •

162   CRFJEZWF EUW JGW AFAEP XURITW

XWJKWWM WLOWURWMVW EMI KRFINC.

          —OGQPPRF JGWUNAL

163   JQNNXMOWW XW COMOSXTXQP

SUI VJO CUAL, CBV XV XW YIXOS VJQV

AOFOPUNW VJO NUROIW US VJO ZXMA.

—ZQITOP NIUBWV

• • • • • • • • • • • • • • • • •

164   JAAZ TAPPBHGTUEGAH GV UV

VEGPBMUEGHJ UV LMUTO TASSCC, UHZ

FBVE UV DUIZ EA VMCCY USECI.

—UHHC PAIIAR MGHZLCIJD

• • • • • • • • • • • • • • • • •

165   VJFZMH ZV J VRMF RE LAJVV,

NBHMHZX KHBRACHMV CR LHXHMJAAT

CZVYRIHM HIHMTKRCT'V EJYH KQF FBHZM

RNX.   —DRXJFBJX VNZEF

166   HJNDN LG GX PQUJ KQLSCQA LM PI

XRNM HJNDN LG XMSI DXXP HX KZVN Z

GLMOSN UQAUZVN.   —AJISSLG CLSSND

• • • • • • • • • • • • • • • • •

167   TGEDPDL AGNOVR QZLLNZFD NR Z

INIAJ-INIAJ BLEBERNANEO MEDRO'A VOET

AGD GZCI EI NA.

—ILZOVCNO B. SEODR

• • • • • • • • • • • • • • • • •

168   QR EUS PDMN NU VDZX IXDSNQRSJ

VSYQL, EUS VSYN KJDE NAX IJDLZ DMC

NAX PAQNX MUNXY NUWXNAXH.

—HQLADHC MQFUM

169   G ZXPL SH GCH XRTLZ CGWL IXVJE
PWLJJ GP PILLR, SVR IXVJE CXR BXPR TGJD
GP WVBT EVZNCF RTL INCRLZ WXCRTP.

—FLXZFL GEL

• • • • • • • • • • • • • • • • •

170   T AFEI F SFN KAFK T SFXX LXFKKINP
CISFRZI TK BIKZ QI MHVAINI.

—AIMMP PHRMBQFM

• • • • • • • • • • • • • • • • •

171   JCQ JZMY FA CFI XYXCIEYA AC LKZL
UY XEJKL KZMY ICAYA ES QYPYXDYI.

—VZXYA X. DZIIEY

172   QLD QDXQ EYJ NLDQLDJ YJ PYQ KYT
GHP LYWZ H IYC XLYTWZ PYQ CD QLD
HJJHPMDRDPQ YE KYTJ GLJYRYXYRDX.

—CDWWH HCATM

• • • • • • • • • • • • • • • • •

173   ULF LFA ICULF LPV KIC DCBEVA
BLZEVKZ, CX INSBN VLBN BCFKLSFZ KNV
EVQ KC KNV CKNVP.   —SZLE ASFVZVF

• • • • • • • • • • • • • • • • •

174   GCTGWAWEHW RL FZJ WCF TN
GJCLVWHREA TFZJCL TN MZWF DTV HTE'F
SJBRJOJ DTVCLJBN.   —WSSW JSWE

175   XOOXEJCPBJBLY QEL XSJLP JIBPUY
TXC IQDLP'J PXJBMLW JIL SBEYJ JBNL
QEXCPW.   —MQJILEBPL WLPLCDL

• • • • • • • • • • • • • • • • •

176   GM HTO RLFE ET VGYY LFH GBJL GF
EIJ RTNYB ETBLH, SJE L XTQQGEEJJ
RTNVGFS TF GE.

—XILNYJW M. VJEEJNGFS

• • • • • • • • • • • • • • • • •

177   KEPX ZWO W KFU OEJCKXQ ZBXA
ZBWU ZX BFAFQXT ZWO PWUBXQ WAT
JFUBXQ QWUBXQ UBWA WKK JWIFQ
VQXTEU VWQTO.   —QFRXQU FQRXA

178   NLJJWO WJ JLXYVQWIN VQTV IL LIY

EBTWXJ VL BWAY—GZV YSYCMGLUM

YIRLMJ.   —RLJYOQ ELICTU

• • • • • • • • • • • • • • • • •

179   BQH'R VQRE SR VM BQEJ MK

ZSBRJNK Q XMTE MK QTV.

—ZJHTL BSNNJT

• • • • • • • • • • • • • • • • •

180   OSRYBFJLD YH BAD VCEG OVVP

PRSJKED DCVRXA BV KDFVND J OJNYEG

ADYSEVVN.   —SRHHDEE KJLDS

181   VNJJD, OCBUJV, MYA UJMNHU GZVH
EJ CYHJOOZDHJA HQ EJ HOZNR JYSQRJA.

—SJMY DMZN OCBUHJO

●●●●●●●●●●●●●●●●●●

182   PRFE XFHLMTZW. VFR'Y DBBTQY XFHL
VFS'M DVGNLDYNFR DM BFRBZHMNJT
TJNVTRBT YKDY XFH DLT EFRVTLWHZ.

—DRR ZDRVTLM

●●●●●●●●●●●●●●●●●●

183   JLXUZELXUHNZUG ZJ QXNG
JLXUZELXU UPHU MSOJ GQS UPL TMQXR
THG.   —T. JQELMJLU EHSRPHE

184   ZGPCMLIARQ ILCVKID UGMRARNR

AM RLDAMV "IGCO ZGMKR AR OKLO" NG

YKGYIK XFG MKJKC BMKX IGCO ZGMKR

XLR LIAJK.   —V.B. UFKRNKCNGM

• • • • • • • • • • • • • • • • • •

185   TH GQPNBL SQV LCDOBZ DO PNB

FLQVN. Q VPEFMKLEMBL XCTIBZ ECP EG Q

SDOZES QOZ GBAA EO NDV ICVNFQLP.

                        —XQFMDB TQVEO

• • • • • • • • • • • • • • • • • •

186   PYZ QM P GQYG KNQDZ ES KPX ISN

RPETNQEX.   —ESR MESKKPNU

187   W TU PBCH EZAK ZE SCXSQ, NXS
AZS TS TYY ZE UTCSHCKZU.

—PZYSTWCB

• • • • • • • • • • • • • • • • •

188   PN DT RXEEIZ SGZ XE TEK ZI IGL
KPNNTLTERTW, XZ MTXWZ DT RXE UTMS
VXOT ZUT DILMK WXNT NIL KPBTLWPZF.

—QIUE N. OTEETKF

• • • • • • • • • • • • • • • •

189   HWBV, EOQLWK UQHYLNLDLHW,
L GZA RHQBVE DH JLIV RHQ EZTA HW
WHDYLWK NOD RHHE ZWE GZDVQ.

—G.B. RLVJEA

190   LKCP LSXCP VS LOSPV, XCP VS
OHVKJ GRJCO JKCX.   —XGC LCTJ

• • • • • • • • • • • • • • • • • •

191   RQEBDXC ZL FCZJX LRDBCP SQ
PCDSO—DJP LDPPNZJX EH DJVGDV.

—YQOJ GDVJC

• • • • • • • • • • • • • • • • • •

192   Z FTJG TECGTPD LZJGI UAW
MWYBZIB UW UFG ATC TIP Z BUTIP CGTPD
UW BTMCZQZMG SD AZQG'B VCWUFGC.

—TCUGSYB ATCP

193   WMP NOUR OFF VNR
ENOAOEVRALXVLEX MK O DMDPFOA
DMFLVLELOG: O NMAALTFR UMLER, TOH
TARRHLGZ, OGH O UPFZOA JOGGRA.

       —OALXVMDNOGRX

• • • • • • • • • • • • • • • • • •

194   SH SNEC VM GJWQ DNX OQWMC
INK WMC BWKHIXE GJWQ DNX IWEE
INK.   —KXQJ SNNKOQVM

• • • • • • • • • • • • • • • • •

195   JI BRSSO JBSIRFB JBA SCWA LMT
YLKK IY L YCMA, YRKK WAMJAMQA CW
KCPA TAYOCMF JBA SIKA IY JCZA CM
BRZLM KCYA.   —PAMMAJB QKLSP

196   OVH OTJYRBH SPOV GJUUPIU PN

OVWO, RX OVH OPEH XJY THWBPQH

XJY'TH IJO PI NVWMH DJT PO, PO'N OJJ

DWT OJ SWBF RWLF.

—DTWIFBPI M. GJIHN

• • • • • • • • • • • • • • • • • •

197   XKQGT'V LNIGXIVX EGSKN-VGJWAL

QIJWZI WV XKUKNNKF.

—XKU FWEVKA

• • • • • • • • • • • • • • • • • •

198   SEC UIPPCUUXIK ZCLVKISDVRJZF DU

J USJSCUHJR, SEC IRUIPPCUUXIK VRC J

PZDHDRJK.   —CZDPE XZVHH

199   BDHMHKV HI PGIN. GFF NAO JA HI
IMGDP GM G QFGKW ILPPM AS TGTPD
OKMHF JDATI AS QFAAJ SADX AK NAOD
SADPLPGJ.   —VPKP SABFPD

• • • • • • • • • • • • • • • • • •

200   LKWFH MNEGWTTHS MECWO WA
AXWT ON OXAOH ALHHOHE, WO
CACXFFI AZNWFA MXAOHE.
                    —XGWVXWF YXS GCEHS

• • • • • • • • • • • • • • • • • •

201   QZJ QFPEYA HCLMFYV ZEHV YZ
YGZAM XGZ HZDM CY, PEJ PFM PHXPVA
FMPJV YZ QIPFJ PEJ JMOMEJ CY.
                    —JPECMH XMLAYMF

202   IATV, ISFV OVCJHLOHRJ MHCM AO
PMSPFVR CHIHN, GLCJ EV JHFVR ZSJM
EISRN DHSJM AO SJ IACVC SJC DIHTAO.

—MVIVR OAZIHRN

• • • • • • • • • • • • • • • • •

203   SU TUYSQTXU XB SWDTNQ FSU HN
WNQTQONV, HKO UXO SU TVNS IGXQN
OTDN GSQ FXDN.   —YTFOXW GKZX

• • • • • • • • • • • • • • • • •

204   OAH UWQH AH OMCNHI WK AXV
AWBWQ OAH KMVOHQ PH DWGBOHI
WGQ VEWWBV.

—QMCEA PMCIW HUHQVWB

205 DXRT EX OBQ MOQB QXEUQRQMBO;
M HRO AMOT QSX GRC ECYXDA.

—KMQR ERX LKBGO

• • • • • • • • • • • • • • • • •

206 ERHX XAOANT IJAKXN TAK PHHFP LA
FHIPKJH KQ, GL'P LGFH LA VRHVS TAKJ
TIJNPLGVS.   —OGCC CHFCHT

• • • • • • • • • • • • • • • • •

207 HIJ OHKUJ SMZGM UHFTB GKTNZU
CWK UMT KHZI YABU IWU RT BAKOKZBTN
ZC ZUB WOOWITIUB RXHYT ZU CWK UMT
NKWALMU.   —NSZLMU S. YWKKWS

208   TB'P YUYCTJM BIYB BIO YUAKJB AH

JOEP BIYB IYVVOJP TJ BIO EAWZX

ONOWD XYD YZEYDP FKPB OLYSBZD HTBP

BIO JOEPVYVOW.   —FOWWD POTJHOZX

• • • • • • • • • • • • • • • • •

209   S FNLVWRDBNJ BD S YBUYZTNX EPTL

QNT S EPLVESEBNJ XP'TP JNE ETKBJU ENN

YSTC EN TPDBDE.   —YWUY SRRPJ

• • • • • • • • • • • • • • • • •

210   YF OCI QVOVSI IRISXPFI HYKK EI

HPSKW-QULPVD QPS QYQOIIF LYFVOID.

—UFWX HUSCPK

211   DAMJS OAM OCHDS FYSNCYZ ANXS
CSNISCJ; DAMJS OAM OCHDS MVJFECSYZ
ANXS FMRRSQDNDMCJ.   —NYVSCD FNREJ

• • • • • • • • • • • • • • • •

212   SJLYSDALSA DY X HJNZAU-DL-BXO
OZJYA KDYDN LAKAU ALGY.

—Z.B. HALSTAL

• • • • • • • • • • • • • • • •

213   QCY VHNPQ CGFV MV MTN FHBYP
HP NTHAYS RI MTN OGNYAQP GAS QCY
PYXMAS CGFV RI MTN XCHFSNYA.

—XFGNYAXY SGNNMK

214   RFCJS FNL BLFQHWE YG MFR EJVYMT
EYLJPHWG, QNR EJMJTYMT RUWE.

—HSMCFM ZFUMGFM

• • • • • • • • • • • • • • • • •

215   UVL BFV ZIFEDWEWVQ
NZUIDNBFVNSWZ WN CFI HLDDLI
DSFV CWCDR ZILFESWVQ WD.

—XVKDL IUEXVL

• • • • • • • • • • • • • • • • •

216   CGXHLN NGEKAZ DQ UJZQ JN
NXUBAQ JN BENNXDAQ, DKC HEC JHF
NXUBAQP.   —JADQPC QXHNCQXH

217   QZHE EZUG PIXAEBL ADDFG UG

NIBD XADNSJILDF SIJUEUPUHAG.

—DFQHBF JHAKJDL

• • • • • • • • • • • • • • • • •

218.   VGC EIH CPLCE GU GC;

VGHDZPIZJGUM GH HGFYSB

ZISGHCEDUGZH VGCE VRPAH.

—ARPRCEB YIPJDP

• • • • • • • • • • • • • • • • •

219   STCHC KTWNEL MC KWYC KBTWWEK

BJEECL LCVWHYJSWHACK SW XTABT

UCWUEC JHC KCOS AV STCZ JHC SWW

PWWL SW MC UHJBSABJE.

—KJYNCE MNSECH

220   GKDCPIYM KFUY RHIY MYYP HQ
RHPYCL SKFM HQ GIDSDGL.

—GFIHCNM GHFSL

● ● ● ● ● ● ● ● ● ● ● ● ● ● ● ● ●

221   CRSJVYJLJ, CRSJMYZDT ZDFLJGZUWJ
ZC VHZMZDT MR UJ NDRVD.

—FHLW CHTHD

● ● ● ● ● ● ● ● ● ● ● ● ● ● ● ● ●

222   LPQMEMCQZR, FSYZ YZUIEKYT PXQZ
MSY JYJQID, UCKY DQP UQQT
MSQPUSMR.

—FCZRMQZ OSPIOSCWW

223   T AKNB EAB ZBLSBHE GTVZFTSTBW
EKO SMLV SML EAB QMNBLCVBCE. JAI
WMC'E EABI UPGE ZLTCE MPL VMCBI JTEA
K LBEPLC KWWLBGG MC TE?

—DMD AMZB

• • • • • • • • • • • • • • • • •

224   PET ZRWTUPWJWR PETIHA W VWYT
NTZP WZ PEFP PET HWUOZ IJ ZFPSHU FHT
RIGLIZTK TUPWHTVA IJ VIZP FWHVWUT
VSOOFOT.   —GFHY HSZZTVV

• • • • • • • • • • • • • • • • •

225   JTTNLZYB CUBLV JTJLNLB; TNLZYB
CUBLV VLBND.   —L.V. BDJUL

226   RMEVPGJP VD DHNPEAVGW UHT
MONVZP VG EAP OZVKPZ CPAVGO UHT,
MGO DJHZG VG EAP HGP MAPMO.

—NMJ NJJFPMZU

• • • • • • • • • • • • • • • • •

227   PRLX DJJLBCFERAJ DXN PRLX KEAQRKJ
RA FGN KRXWQ. JVXLO FGNB RSS NTNXP
RAVN EA D KGEWN, RX FGN WEYGF
KRA'F VRBN EA.   —DWDA DWQD

• • • • • • • • • • • • • • • • •

228   BOIM QEM QGLO YXLI BOXYNQ
EVPGB TIPTHI EB BOIXA JGYIAEHQ BOEB
XB RESIQ RI QEW BOEB X'R NPXYN BP
RXQQ RXYI VM KGQB E JIF WEMQ.

—NEAAXQPY SIXHHPA

229   YFW PCJBW XR AXYFXM HCG. PCJBW
HCGJRWVP.   —FSJJXRCM PCJO

• • • • • • • • • • • • • • • • •

230   EUJ'P OJUNO PCQ DQZPCQH; JKJQ-
PQJPCI UM PCQ XQUXRQ NUFREJ'P IPZHP
Z NUJWQHIZPKUJ KM KP EKEJ'P NCZJYQ
UJNQ KJ Z DCKRQ.   —OKJ CFAAZHE

• • • • • • • • • • • • • • • • •

231   STFLJIY NUAO TYG FUODYOC RYL
JTLU S KSX LURYLZYO GJLZUAL SORAJTR, S
XSTD OUXXYOF ZSC WACL LSDYT VMSKY.
                        —WUZTTF KSOCUT

232   DU WNMUMIGKC GK DU WYJWQC

BPM BGZZ XUMB CMIMQQMB BPL CPW

CPGUFK PW JQWHGNCWH LWKCWQHDL

HGHU'C PDJJWU.   —WDQZ BGZKMU

● ● ● ● ● ● ● ● ● ● ● ● ● ● ● ● ●

233   BRXMV FMQYZ JY XPM VJBN KJ IOAP

Q UBYX XJ KWMYN IJVM XQIM UQXP IE

RBIQDE, UPJ Q PMBV BVM UJYNMVROD

WMJWDM.   —PJUQM IBYNMD

● ● ● ● ● ● ● ● ● ● ● ● ● ● ● ● ●

234   NJD HMG IJC VR RPSRHARK AJ

YJERTG M HJCGATI ANMA NML ADJ

NCGKTRK MGK BJTAI-LXP QXGKL JB

HNRRLR?   —HNMTORL KR YMCOOR

235   ATCI TX ATJI H G-QWMTI. ZWE
LWK'V NHKV VW AIHMI TK VPI QTLLAI WC
TV, GEV ZWE LWK'V NHKV VW XII TV
HOHTK.   —VIL VEUKIU

• • • • • • • • • • • • • • • • • •

236   GA GAPA IS NSSP GA KJE TS KSW
GJWAP. ZRW CW ECET'W QJWWAP
ZAUJRIA GA KJE TS ZJWKWRZ WS NRW
CW CT JTMGJM.   —WSQ EPAAIAT

• • • • • • • • • • • • • • • • • •

237   AUT YBTLYCT KTEFOI OM MTBTE
OEFUTM IQEC, ROAU VSMA Y UYID-OEFU
TLYMTL—OE FYMT ZQS AUQSCUA
QKAOXOMX RYM JTYJ.   —LQHTLA HLYSIA

238   DRPP ZPRQOMQ'H KMYGRNQ
BMPRZS GEBGYRGQZG HOGUH UXRQPS
KYMU WXLRQN DYGXTKXHO XO OWG
RQOGYQXORMQXP WMAHG MK
BXQZXTGH.   —BXO DAZWXQXQ

• • • • • • • • • • • • • • • • •

239   RPEAZPA FDZARKRVZARQP AZJME
AQQ HQPF.   —VZDDRM KRETMD

• • • • • • • • • • • • • • • •

240   JU AWZ SC YW YXFR YW UWK, XEB
UWKG AWZ SC YW FSCYDE. SH UWK
HSESCO HSGCY, VFDXCD FDY JD REWM.
                —OXGGU ODGCOHSDFB

241   SAQ SL BM ZYVQL TQRTQIX JDTVAR
BM MQWTX VA IYQ IYQWIQT VX IYWI V
ZSDOJA'I XVI VA IYQ WDJVQAZQ WAJ
HWIZY BQ.   —KSYA EWTTMBSTQ

• • • • • • • • • • • • • • • • • •

242   F ANVQ QH B YNOQBWYBVQ QGBQ
ONYPNO LYNBJMBOQ BQ BVD QFSN. OH
F HYTNYNT MYNVUG QHBOQ TWYFVX
QGN YNVBFOOBVUN.

                    —OQNPNV AYFXGQ

• • • • • • • • • • • • • • • • • •

243   VMND PNRR SFWFZ AF T
QNWNRNIFY QHBSVZU BSVNR PF DOFSY
JHZF JHSFU LHZ AHHXD VMTS PF YH LHZ
QMFPNSE EBJ.   —FRAFZV MBAATZY

244 ARYFCG AH ARI BFAIPGAYAI RBLRVYU
GUGAIJ, BA BG FHV DHGGBZEI AH
APYOIE XPHJ THYGA AH THYGA VBARHWA
GIIBFL YFUARBFL. —TRYPEIG CWPYEA

• • • • • • • • • • • • • • • • •

245 ZAZ ENJ VOVT GYQB AD Y TNNU
YDZ CNTSVF GRE ENJ GYQBVZ AD? A
FRADB FRYF'H RNG ZNSH HWVDZ FRVAT
QAOVH. —HJV UJTWRE

• • • • • • • • • • • • • • • • •

246 WUBYN YAB VWSB AYRRWGN. PTE
IBG Y LTEOVB YCU VBYAC QTX GT
QYCUVB GQBJ, YCU OABGGP NTTC PTE
QYZB Y UTFBC. —HTQC NGBWCRBLS

247   Z FCPHK'Y LHMGLYHI NA NZBBZKT
WLHIZY WCLI YG YFH MGJZWH
QHWCEBH SFGHPHL BYGJH ZY ZB
BMHKIZKT JHBB YFCK NA SZDH.

—ZJZH KCBYCBH

• • • • • • • • • • • • • • • • •

248   OXK DKAO FZC OG BKKW HXLTSQKR
XGVK LA OG VZBK OXK XGVK
ZOVGAWXKQK WTKZAZRO—ZRS TKO OXK
ZLQ GIO GY OXK OLQKA.

—SGQGOXC WZQBKQ

• • • • • • • • • • • • • • • • •

249   VMS JMTWAO UDTUAD ET TWZ FHO
UFS ZT JDD NFO KTIBDJ VMDH ZMDS QFH
JZFS FZ MTKD FHO JDD NFO ZDADIBJBTH
GTP HTZMBHE?   —JFKWDA ETAOVSH

250   TMGELP T FXYGELP FYEVCY FOTV OC

VOELGM TAXNV HYEVEHM EM ZEGC

TMGELP T ZTIBBXMV OXF EV DCCZM

TAXNV QXPM.

—HOYEMVXBOCY OTIBVXL

• • • • • • • • • • • • • • • •

251   S'Z ESYX PT VXX PNX CTAXGKJXKP

CXP TWP TU OMG MEPTCXPNXG MKZ

EXMAX PNX ONTEX USXEZ PT HGSAMPX

SKZWVPGQ.   —RTVXHN NXEEXG

• • • • • • • • • • • • • • • •

252   RSPQXW, FE GFTKPX, JDP LJX YXPL

GDPLSQA. SE JX RFXPQ'L OSVX DQ DGLFK

JX PSIHOW LXDKP JSI TH.

—DOEKXR JSLGJGFGV

253   F CVTOY OCPL VODCWSZ CXSEW

LFV HZOQOZODPOV QSZ WLO

HZOVFYODPM, CDY DFDOWM-VFA

VODCWSZV OCPL ZOPOFROY SDO RSWO.

—BSLD Q. TODDOYM

• • • • • • • • • • • • • • • • • •

254   KZBBTR MPR: USRI LQO'GR SQKR

QI NMAOGBML IZPSA, ASR ARTRDSQIR

GZIPN, MIB LQO SQDR ZA'N ASR UGQIP

IOKJRG.   —GZIP TMGBIRG

• • • • • • • • • • • • • • • • • •

255   L CILGD YZG BIR IWFZ W MLZTNZJ

ZWT WTZ VZCCZT MTZMWTZJ KRT

YWTTLWEZ. CIZU'FZ ZPMZTLZGNZJ MWLG

WGJ VRHEIC OZBZQTU.   —TLCW THJGZT

256   VEI'LR ETNV QRLR JEL U WQELC
KDWDC. SET'C QILLV. SET'C HELLV. UTS
ZR WILR CE WGRNN CQR JNEHRLW UNETF
CQR HUV.   —HUNCRL QUFRT

• • • • • • • • • • • • • • • • •

257   QEYYEBOU YBOZ LBK EQQBKXFYEXR
SVB MB OBX HOBS SVFX XB MB SEXV
XVJQUJYNJU BO F KFEOR UDOMFR
FLXJKOBBO.   —UDUFO JKXW

• • • • • • • • • • • • • • • • •

258   ND PRJ RCQ PRJL KHUT H VJUSLQS
IRJUSE, PRJ VHBQ H ILRKFQX; KJZ ND PRJ
RCQ PRJL KHUT H XNFFNRU, NZ VHE.
                    —ARVU XHPUHLS TQPUQE

259   QTJ UNXQJXQ SNC QK XZGGJJL AX
QK MKKY NX AU CKZ NFJ HMNCAWP VC
KQTJF HJKHMJ'X FZMJX, STAMJ EZAJQMC
HMNCAWP VC CKZF KSW.

—OAGTNJM YKFLN

• • • • • • • • • • • • • • • •

260   EFDC FU OBFOEB DIZKG DIBN'MB
LIYMZDYJEB ZU DIBN PZHB YSYN DIBZM
FEX LEFDIBC YKX DIZKPC DIBN XFK'D
SYKD.   —VNMDEB MBBX

• • • • • • • • • • • • • • • •

261   ANZXZ'H HM YQVN KJIHAFV FE
ANFH VQJAQXZ ANIA BFESJ JZMKIXP
HUFE FH GZVMYFER IE ZEPIERZXZP
HSEANZAFV.   —JFJS AMYJFE

262   LE CDZ QLMX YD YWX ITX DE I
WZOSFXS CDZ WIMX LY GISX VXNIZAX
MXFC EXP KXDKQX SLX KIAY YWX ITX DE
I WZOSFXS.   —TXDFTX VZFOA

• • • • • • • • • • • • • • • • • •

263   ZIKGUVHV VGACN IXSTH CUCAHQ
GAKLACH SJ HZAUK OUMAV HTCUCW
HZAUK ZIKGV ICN HAC GAKLACH
GOIQUCW STH SJ HTCA.

—UWSK VHKIMUCVYQ

• • • • • • • • • • • • • • • • • •

264   UYAIKLP ZG CUFUYC L TZVUIURULY
INK HKDA IZ INK RUID, UI QUCNI EK
EKIIKX IZ RNLYCK INK VZRHA.

—PZSC VLXAZY

265   NZCCOYZZA'U M FCMJH YNHVH

BNHO'CC FMO OZT M BNZTUMLA

AZCCMVU QZV M PWUU, MLA QWQBO

JHLBU QZV OZTV UZTC.

—EMVWCOL EZLVZH

• • • • • • • • • • • • • • • • •

266   AN VSM XMHMJ GKFPNX, AJTE

GAIME SFG F XSFHMJ NFOM. VSDX

XSACTG VMTT CX XABMVSDJQ FRACV

VSM OCXVAB AN XSFHDJQ.

—VAB PARRDJX

• • • • • • • • • • • • • • • • •

267   U CEHN YNAK PBXNBF KP TN

EVEQNRNX EK ERD KUIN UR SEFN PA

REKUPREY NINBMNRSD, NHNR UA U'I UR

E SETURNK INNKURM.   —BPREYX BNEMER

268   C KROCJIQR YJFD BCX PD RQD
KQMORDKR TJKRCFED PDRVDDF RVM
SMJFRK, PZR JR JK PX FM BDCFK RQD
BMKR JFRDODKRJFI.   —TMERMO VQM

• • • • • • • • • • • • • • • • •

269   X'Y TKLKZVXW KOVGE NHNLPEJXZS.
VZ YP MEKEXVZKLP OXIPIQN X JKHN K
LNKLHXNC YXLLVL.   —LXIJKLW QNCXM

• • • • • • • • • • • • • • • • •

270   J TIIF DZWKVXVS ZW XIK WIGVIXV
NZKP XIKPZXT KI WJU. J TIIF DZWKVXVS
ZW J TIIF KJDQVS NZKP J WISV KPSIJK.
                    —QJKPJSZXV NPZKVPISX

271   ZUYUDAUYO DSWPYV UY FAS
PQJXNUWD OSFD JPL DUQISK.
ZUYUDAUYO DSWPYV UY NPQUFUWD
OSFD JPL PTQUIUPY.

—KUWACKV XUQAPLD YUBPY

• • • • • • • • • • • • • • • • •

272   E FA PWX MEKKEPT XW SECN XOZ
KEYZC WR TZSAFP CWKHEZSC RWS
BWQPXSEZC MOWCZ PFAZC MZ BFPPWX
CDZKK DSWDZSKL.   —YWKNZS SQOZ

• • • • • • • • • • • • • • • • •

273   PRF KGZQFTP BGUJ YZ PRF FZQKYTR
KDZQMDQF YT PRF GZF PRDP WGKKGBT
PRF NRUDTF, "DZJ ZGB D BGUJ WUGL
GMU TNGZTGU."   —RDK FDPGZ

274   LKLG WUAL LFVYOLAVZMGE ZPVG

ZPL EQI BPU ZPMGSY PL SGUBY MZ VRR

MY ZPL UGL BPU ALVRRI NULY.

—VR CLAGYZLMG

• • • • • • • • • • • • • • • • •

275   J EDMP HEFRXB LQ ZJGC I CPB EY

HIBBPUJPC YEU MXUJCBLIC VJBX I DEBP

ED JB CIQJDR, "BEQC DEB JDMTFGPG."

—HPUDIUG LIDDJDR

• • • • • • • • • • • • • • • • •

276   PWLCFUOH DUO GWO IVTG

FOTLUDXCO VNNVHOHGT DG TPUDXXCO

DT GWOA DUO XVGW ODTA GV XODG

DHF RZH GV PWODG.

—RUDH COXVSLGE

277   IZX VAWN SLBV IAX HZUKO BPZ

XAWHK'O JWZUBZOB SLBLZO LI BPZ

IDQEZW AT MZAMHZ UWADIK XPAQ VAD

OPADHKI'B QUNZ U ODKKZI QARZ.

—KURLK HZBBZWQUI

• • • • • • • • • • • • • • • • •

278   DAG TU QBKTL LBMW BM HAN

JUKMBMW? BH'L HAN HKBXJSAIMH

LAUXH: "DN WUH HAKUXWA IMUHANK

MBWAH."   —NMBT QIWMUOT

• • • • • • • • • • • • • • • • •

279   UN UOV VRRZDZPQQS WPQMN

RKNNHVL VR AINNDO PFVWN QZRN

ZEANQR ANNL EV OPWN YVEOZYJ EV

EPQC PFVME FME EON UNPEONK.

—FPKFPKP NOKNYKNZDO

280   XKA X QXF PGBSG PXJ GL BK VDBFV
ZD RDZL, XFI GL PBWW TNDCXCWJ ZLWW
JDE. XKA GBQ, GDPLRLN, PGJ, XFI
RXVELFLKK BK XWW.   —CLNFXNI WLRBF

• • • • • • • • • • • • • • • • •

281   DUKPLVLA GQXW EQXCK MEVUK
GQXW SVBC PWK CZVUU AWQMVLA VC
UVSK CEQRKUVLA ZEK MPUS JKNQWK VZ
CZQIC CLQMVLA.

                              —IEGUUVC BVUUKW

• • • • • • • • • • • • • • • • •

282   E THRXPHRDVY DV QGY EPQ HU
CDKDCDZW E TEFY DZ VITG E AEN QGEQ
YKYPNHZY MYBDYKYV GY GEV QGY
MDWWYVQ XDYTY.   —BICADW YPGEPC

283   O'K S DVOZBNBDVG KSTBQ. PVSP

KYSIN O FSI PVOIE WYYD PVBJXVPN

SMBJP MYOIX JIYKDZBGYW.

—MQJFY ZYY

• • • • • • • • • • • • • • • • •

284   VD INWWTCNNJ, ED GUFVLEXWG

JVONHKG MGLLWGAGDL AGEDM GEKI

REHLT BGLLVDB PVPLT RGHKGDL NP LIG

RFXWVKVLT.   —WEFHGD XEKEWW

• • • • • • • • • • • • • • • • •

285   PMQJ ECQD MWJ M RQCROQ

LQMKO CL KAWJ RQORMQO ZCN LCQ

VPO GNFDZ UQOMDH VPMV LAWMGGZ

FCKO MGCWT—CQ JCW'V.

—PMQQAHCW LCQJ

286   W'FJ QVWUJM V RJE ZNTUMC
VGNTUM HAJ PWMMKJ. HAJ NUKB KNEJG-
ONMB QVGPJUHC W NEU HAVH CHWKK
RWH PJ YNPRNGHVOKB VGJ HNEJKC.

—MVFJ OVGGB

• • • • • • • • • • • • • • • • •

287   SHIHK AKMP MAJTX ZJTK MSLHYXJKY
LJEQSP JIHK JS XCH EMZODJVHK; XCH
QEEQPKMXQJS DMVY VHKHS'X MY
YXKQLX QS XCJYH NMZY.   —DHV DHCK

• • • • • • • • • • • • • • • • •

288   ZF'C CFAIQBN WKY LNY KL FWN
YKAUT'C BANIF MAKRUNHC IAN CKUJNT
RG MNKMUN YWK ANHNHRNA FWNZA
IUBNRAI.   —WNARNAF MAKDWQKY

289   IVXC FKPC QKZCA UXJCIFN, EJIOKXI
RBWWCVA KV TFBAOJWD FJDOIA. JT NKX
OCBV RCFFA, DCI NKXV CBVA QOCQMCY.

                —CVJQO ACDBF

• • • • • • • • • • • • • • • • •

290   SR DHM CHU'J XBUJ JH XHNA, DHM
GBKV JH XHNA JH VBNU VUHMFG EHUVD
OH JGBJ DHM XHU'J GBKV JH XHNA.

                —HFCVU UBOG

• • • • • • • • • • • • • • • • •

291   NWZONAZUNJA NM Z OJJV LJPMG
UJ KZPPH HJR JSGP ULG OPJRAV—AJU Z
DCHNAO KZPXGU UJ MGU HJR DPGG
DPJW XPJTZTNCNUH.

             —PJTGPUMJA VZSNGM

292 JEQBDP JFO JBTJWP JPZGHX BGDDBO

ZGEP TKJD DKOW TJHD DL NO TKOH

DKOW XFLT QV—'AJQPO DKOW'FO

BLLZGHX MLF GEOJP.

—VJQBJ VLQHEPDLHO

• • • • • • • • • • • • • • • • • •

293 L ZETUQCZ QC L XBRREY YNE

IUQABC ZNETCLPIC EX FQRBC CE NB JLP

WB GNEZEOULGNBI CZLPIQPO QP XUEPZ

EX NQC JLU.   —BFQRB OLPBCZ

• • • • • • • • • • • • • • • • • •

294 REI'J RJ EJGKIVC? JFC EKTC OCXOHC

MFX HKAVF KJ VWOEW BXGJAIC JCHHCGE

JKDC CQXIXTREJE ECGRXAEHW.

—QRIQRIIKJR CIYARGCG

295   HSZXSB ANX KHZK IJKGSBKKUBS
YBHC GS THLOK, SXO TGLOGXS, NHK
SBMBQ QBHY XCY TGMB-ZBHQ
VQXDBLOGXSK.   —UHCLXCU TXQIBK

• • • • • • • • • • • • • • • • • •

296   Q'K FQSJP VM WGG FLQY DVDYJDYJ
WNVTF NJWTFI NJQDZ VDGI YEQD PJJH.
FLWF'Y PJJH JDVTZL. XLWF PV IVT XWDF,
WD WPVSWNGJ HWDRSJWY?

—BJWD EJSS

• • • • • • • • • • • • • • • • • •

297   SXNJHPG JWLOSWN RN JSLJ DWU
LUY ULJXHUN TWSLCW FXNWBG HUOW
JSWG SLCW WQSLRNJWY LBB HJSWP
LBJWPULJXCWN.   —LTTL WTLU

298   VGZD ELZ IPXQU EFED FXVG ILXMZ-
XQB. QPF FGZLZ ELZ VGZ VZZQEUZLB
UPXQU VP UP VP QPV FEVNG E RPMXZ?

—TPT VGPREB

• • • • • • • • • • • • • • • • •

299   GZIV GZH FHYNGZ SZ O RUGLNOZP
SN O QGYH, OZP UH SN SZRHYHNRSZJ
QHMOLNH UH SN GZH FHYNGZ SZ O
RUGLNOZP.   —UOYGIP ZSMGINGZ

• • • • • • • • • • • • • • • • •

300   KRSP HP HDI SCPM CV VGMYW
WIOCYX WH PCYF VHLMWKCYX WH FH
UCWK WKM WCLM UM KRQM IDVKMF
WKIHDXK SCPM WIOCYX WH VRQM.

—UCSS IHXMIV

301   XZY CFKCHXCSY EO ZCKQHS C ACF
VYVEIU QN XZCX, NYKYICW XQVYN EKYI,
EHY YHGEUN XZY NCVY SEEF XZQHSN
OEI XZY OQINX XQVY.

—OIQYFIQJZ HQYXDNJZY

• • • • • • • • • • • • • • • • •

302   JMUX, AJ KJB LUBH LUI VQEAS, WYS
BJHAI'S HRHEXJIH LUMH U EJYKG BEUVS
WHVJEH SGHX LUMH U LUASHENQHFH?

—FJYESIHX GYASJI

• • • • • • • • • • • • • • • • •

303   QP KEKAKNO DXTGBETX INT AB TSX
WXD ZBD HXZNQNAKBE BZ UWNDNUAXD,
YSA AWXE K DXNOKRXH AWNA K WNH EB
UWNDNUAXD.   —UWNDOXT YNDVOXP

304   CVXGVYW DOVTVT VT MBUM
CZCWIM PBWI QZS OWUGVFW QZSO
DBVGXOWI UIX QZSO DGZMBWT UOW
UKZSM MBW TUCW UNW.

—KVGG MUCCWST

• • • • • • • • • • • • • • • • •

305   YHRTMBUQD PWNN KUCUQ
QUTNJYU BEU PJDBULJDOUB PEUK WB
YHRUD BH DBQUJRNWKWKZ HSSWYU
PHQO.   —YNJVBHK UNPUNN

• • • • • • • • • • • • • • • • •

306   ECYOY SD HKECSHA XKOY
XSDYOBZRY SH ECY FKORP ECBH EK
BOOSNY SH WBOBPSDY BHP RKKQ RSQY
UKVO WBDDWKOE WCKEK.

—YOXB ZKXZYGQ

307   VMJ VKTOAZJ ISVM WTYV TP OY SY
VMNV IJ ITOZR KNVMJK AJ KOSFJR AL
DKNSYJ VMNF YNQJR AL UKSVSUSYW.

—FTKWNF QSFUJFV DJNZJ

· · · · · · · · · · · · · · · · ·

308   UPTMEVS LGUZ OP MEV EXQUP
DEUSUDMVS OH MEUM VIVSKWTFK
ZUPMH MT WXOGF UPF PTWTFK ZUPMH
MT FT QUOPMVPUPDV.

—JXSM ITPPVAXM

· · · · · · · · · · · · · · · · ·

309   MEB JBLXBNNPTC MEPTC WYSRM
MBTTPN PN MEWM TS AWMMBX ESF CSSJ
P CBM, P'DD TBZBX YB WN CSSJ WN W
FWDD.   —APMUE EBJYBXC

310   YA TDV JZB KABXKJ BNA DPPAFBHZJ
ZP BNZLA YNZ CHEA XL, OXB YA DCYDVL
KALUAFB BNAHK QZZI WXIQTAJB.

—CHOOHA PXIHT

•••••••••••••••••

311   CSDB ASMZQV HZC DJHLPICLME
VICDA ME RQMCSDA AM TD TMZQV YEMT
TSDE CSDB KM MZC MN ACBQD.

—KIPPB ASIEVQLEK

•••••••••••••••••

312   P GSIY YD T BPRB XABDDC YBTY GTX
XD MTIRSFDJX, YBS XABDDC ISGXWTWSF
BTM TI DOPYJTFQ ADCJVI.

—FDANQ FTQ

313   DPWH-FXDMXKWXEP XD BYPE VAGT

MAEDMXPEMP QPWWD VAG QA FA

DASPQYXEJ REF VAG FAE'Q QRWL ZRML.

—B.L. YAKP

• • • • • • • • • • • • • • • • • •

314   KFECJ KX UMLC JEB GBJ Q XBKA

UKAM AUE ZQKFX EV ZQCAX, QCI AMLC

GBFC Q MEPL KC AML DEQA.

—PQBFLCDL ZLALF

• • • • • • • • • • • • • • • • • •

315   V GWHAWU'N USEDAVALWJ LN FVGS

RT AYS JDFRSU WQ SFLJSJA FSJ KYW GLS

DJGSU YLN HVUS.

—CSWUCS RSUJVUG NYVK

316   A PADVYF UZFT JL ZVKHQTE WBJFK
ZBJF PYBJ UBYO, AP CZF OAEK QYF
KCASS QSAMF, CZFT A'MF EBTF JL RBH.

                              —YBKFQTTF FYQBSE

• • • • • • • • • • • • • • • • •

317   TIY DGL JT ATTV TXJ MTO
YIBFIYYOL—JDYN PYBFI RFJD LYRFIB
CGQDFIYL GIK YIK XH RFJD JDY GJTCFQ
PTCP.   —CGOQYA HGBITA

• • • • • • • • • • • • • • • • •

318   EB E MRRAEDRU, W ZEB LNUR NK EA
EAEUQXWBM, OCM ANZ W ZEAM VRNVYR
MN MXUWTR EAP OR XEULNAWNCB.

                              —AWQNYEB QEDR

319   LI WZNC, X EZYZC CZNVXUZW TING
N GZCCXFVZ VLG LQ ZRSVNXEXEA LEZ
INK GL WL XE N HMCWZC!

—NANGIN BICXKGXZ

• • • • • • • • • • • • • • • • •

320   T KILPAIO NR CMN NWI NRTKIN
FILN ORYA. TN XLJIF SRM KRRJ KTJI L
YLPX, BLPTAZ, FIAFTNTQI WMXLA GITAZ.

—PLKCW ARGKI

• • • • • • • • • • • • • • • • •

321   BMJBWH DP VQYP SC SLCHP
WCIVFPX SLBV WCI, DPYBIHP SLPW BXP
SLP CVPH JLC JQMM DP JXQSQVF BDCIS
WCI.   —YWXQM YCVVCMMW

322   W OWYMKH PWBWFMQG MR QGA
JXACA HQZ WCCMPA JMFX OMPA EWVR,
OQZC DMIR WGI RAPAG M-FXQZVXF-HQZ-
TWBDAI-MFR.   —MPACG EWKK

• • • • • • • • • • • • • • • • • •

323   HKO ISJCH CSLW GI NYHBJSHQ SC
HKO TSCDGUOJQ HKYH HKO UGPBNO
AWGE YPCG HBJWC HG HKO POIH.

—DKSDYLG HJSEBWO

• • • • • • • • • • • • • • • • • •

324   MWS BNC'G NPUNME IW XM
VTJVAG WJKCKWC. N GSAZVM, KH MWS
NEZ N GSAZVM, ERWSPL XV EGSHHVL
UKGR IANEERWJJVAE, IAKG, NCL UWAOE.

—NCWCMOWSE

325   LYCCKYJS KG QKXS DAKCQKPJ Y

IYDVP, DZCPKPJ FYPOGMCKPJG, VC

SYDKPJ AKDF BFVMGDKBXG. KD QVVXG

SYGR ZPDKQ RVZ DCR KD.

—FSQSP CVAQYPO

• • • • • • • • • • • • • • • • •

326   TWKI XPN FKCJW GPF LWK ZLCFZ,

XPN YCX IPL ONRLK QKL PIK, ANL XPN

TPI'L JPYK NB TRLW C WCISGNM PG YNS

KRLWKF.   —MKP ANFIKLL

• • • • • • • • • • • • • • • • •

327   D ZBCT MF D LDP ENB FUTPVF FB

LXIN AMLT ADWSMPJ DZBXA NMLFTWG

ANDA OBX IDP'A ADWS DZBXA

OBXCFTWG.   —LTWQMWWT WDPVBP

328   QAPP HWZ JZEJPZ AG HWZ BWZUJZT

FZUHF BPUJ DERT WUGSF? UPP HWZ TZFH

EO DER, AO DER'PP XRFH TUHHPZ DERT

XZQZPTD.   —XEWG PZGGEG

• • • • • • • • • • • • • • • • •

329   P OLSTQLO P'X MUQPW MJ

KUZXPWQ Z ESUR MJ VLZHUVEUZKU, MTO

OLUW P OLSTQLO, DLJ VLSTYX P? LU

WUNUK KUZXV ZWJ SC RPWU.

                            —VEPHU RTYYPQZW

• • • • • • • • • • • • • • • • •

330   WZS NTVSG L YGNM, WZS TSHH

LJFNGWCUW WZS ONJJC QSONJSH.

TSW WZS GSCVSG OCWOZ ZLH NMU

QGSCWZ.

                            —STLICQSWZ OTCGPHNU IMCGW

331   PMLOKTLOP KNO ROPK ZGI KM
BMDYTDBO PMLOMDO NO TP ZFMDW
TP KM AOK NTL NGYO NTP ZGI.

—FOS M'SMDDOAA

• • • • • • • • • • • • • • • • • •

332   CVNAVME VF XVRO B FYVUOP'F JOK,
BAABNQOU OLOP FM FXVIQAXH
YOPQBYF, KZA FAVXX BAABNQOU AM
XVCO BA BXX CMZP NMPEOPF.

—LVPIVEVB JMMXC

• • • • • • • • • • • • • • • • • •

333   P UCNIZ LC TIA ECBV WPLE RCB UE
GIFHLG. P'U SFBFTCPZ FTZ TIA ECBV AFX
LGI CTHE SHFWI AGIBI UE RIFBX AIBI
QDXLPRPIZ.   —FTPLF AIPXX

334   SUE VYIYH GYY P NPV DPRBZVM
QUDV CAY GCHYYC DZCA P DUNPV DAU
APG P RZCCRY WUCLYRRS PVQ P LPRQ
GWUC.   —YRPSVY LUUGRYH

· · · · · · · · · · · · · · · · · ·

335   QS KRPOMLTB GVJRZ PN MR ATXIZ
XVR QS IGEKQTERB GKZ P UTIZ MPQ TN
ATXBVR MR ATXIZ, VT ITKO GV MR ZPZK'U
UGJR PU TXU TN QS OGBZRK.

—RBPA QTBRAGQLR

· · · · · · · · · · · · · · · · · ·

336   ULM MB UZH ZYAXHJU LMAXJ SF UZH
HFRKSJZ KYFRGYRH UM AZCNH YAH KSBH
YFX KMWH—MB YKK LMAXJ.

—JUHDZHF JMFXZHSN

337   SRCMCZCA L RCDA DMGBMC
DAWHLMW OBA IEDZCAG, L OCCE D
IJABMW LUNHEIC JB ICC LJ JALCF BM RLU
NCAIBMDEEG.   —DKADRDU ELMVBEM

• • • • • • • • • • • • • • • • •

338   MTK WKNA FNGQKW VH GPM MTNM
IPDRSMKWH ZVAA UKQVG MP MTVGX
AVXK DKG, USM MTNM DKG ZVAA UKQVG
MP MTVGX AVXK IPDRSMKWH.

—HEFGKE TNWWVH

• • • • • • • • • • • • • • • •

339   HMEJ NF NXJMCY ZCAVCPCS EZXDJ
QXXBVKO VI JMEJ VL FXD HXYBCS MEYS
EKS GYXIGCYCS, IXNCXKC CAIC HXDAS
SX VJ LXY FXD.   —KXYE CGMYXK

340   BRT UYTV MYO UTITMU QIYM XTBSV,
NQO QIYM OTCITSBCTMO BMU WTBAOW.
VYCT CTM BST NYSM YAU, BMU VYCT
MTHTS RSYP VY.   —OSXYM TUPBSUV

• • • • • • • • • • • • • • • • • •

341   R KCWPCT WRE USTL OJF VJFPRYMF,
USP RE RTWOJPMWP WRE CEBL RKQJFM
OJF WBJMEP PC ZBREP QJEMF.

                    —HTREY BBCLK NTJIOP

• • • • • • • • • • • • • • • • • •

342   CM NPF JGCDJ PSS NOGDJ PM
RH ZGSSVJV CDMVOTCVN IDMCS C
DGDZLPSPDMSH PFYVE, "EG HGI DVVE
PDH SPOJV EGDPMCGDF AGO DVN
KICSECDJF?"   —MGEE PDEVOFGD

343   QE QF FRXVGA ECNE GOR MNUEF

GO TGGV ERUAF, IRLNKFR QZ GOR PRUR

GO TGGV ERUAF GOR PGKXV OGE MNUE.

—ANULRX MUGKFE

• • • • • • • • • • • • • • • • • •

344   HK UMLPMJ DEYW HW ROB HMCPGR

PM AOYW, QVP XGWC O LMVAUC'P NEK

PGW QOAA GW DEYW HW ROB HMCPGR

HMJW.   —XEAPWJ HEPPGEV

• • • • • • • • • • • • • • • • • •

345   PZFYF'N IXF PZBXM OTIDP

QZBVSYFX—PZFE XFAFY MI OYIDXS

NZIJBXM NXOHNZIPN IW PZFBY

MYOXSHOYFXPN.   —TFNNBF & TFDVOZ

346   WHSW RO WZA LHLA HXRCRWM WP
EAAD ORCAVW UZRCA WUP YLRAVKO HLA
HLIGRVI, HVK MPG EVPU XPWZ PY WZAB
HLA ULPVI.   —ZGIZ HCCAV

• • • • • • • • • • • • • • • • •

347   UGVMCMTC MT D RNSSQKAX KQDCS
UK CMWB VNDV SWDLXST D VSDHSVVXS
VU TMWY VNUAYN MW NUV JDVSQ AG
VU MVT WUTS.   —NDQUXB NSXKSQ

• • • • • • • • • • • • • • • • •

348   FDFM KDFBVFQYXI URIA
QMAIQMUIQDFCO TMKV IXF URBNQMRC
BHCF: VXFM LRI, RBBRMYF OKHBAFCL QM
ACQG ZKAFA.   —EKXM VFQIJ

349 LUWWUP OZPOZ MO VYZ WUOV
ZBZPHN IMOVJMAXVZI TXGPVMVN MP
VYZ EUJHI. ZBZJNUPZ VYMPQO YZ YGO
ZPUXCY.   —JZPZ IZOLGJVZO

• • • • • • • • • • • • • • • • • •

350 QTC RSXWQ QSNC S UCVQ QM BV
BNCXSABV XCWQBGXBVQ, QTCF BWZCY,
"TMU NBVF BXC SV FMGX DBXQF?" S
WBSY, "QUM NSHHSMV."

                    —FBZMP WNSXVMRR

• • • • • • • • • • • • • • • • • •

351 X ATFH SEPXKHL PATP PAH NHENGH
ZAE TUH GTPH TUH EMPHS YE WJKA
QEGGXHU PATS PAH NHENGH ZAE ATFH
PE ZTXP MEU PAHW.   —H.F. GJKTY

352   LIRJNAEANU AD JGGYOAZF
YZRDRGK NY XJSR XADNJSRD. JIN AD
SZYOAZF OCALC YZRD NY SRRW.

—DLYNN JQJXD

•••••••••••••••••

353   MUTLJUO WIEJ I UIUJ QFMJU PFL
STEJP LF IPGFPJ JKOJ; MJ VIP HFUJ QJFQKJ
KFPS IDLJU MJ IUJ BJIB.

—OTPVKITU KJMTO

•••••••••••••••••

354   TNVIL N'GL KLIRSL X ILVBEXQ
KXVJLE, N'GL QLXEVLW BR SASKQL
HNBO ZELXB IROLELVIL.

—XQXV ZELLVTYXV

355   HFZHVF PRZ ROAF UZ PFONUFQQFQ
OKF MFKKCEVF; MRFKF CQ UZ POD ZG
MONCUS OIAOUMOSF ZG MRFW.

—OUOMZVF GKOUXF

• • • • • • • • • • • • • • • •

356   VWN LNSCPR JPCV ENPEHN EHSX
IPHO MC VP TNSL ZHPVWNC VWNX
TPFHU RPV DN ZSFIWV UNSU MR
PVWNLTMCN.   —LPINL CMJPR

• • • • • • • • • • • • • • • •

357   OIBX BX V QCSS ZEMWOCG. QEPJX
IVTS V CBKIO OE XSWF YS PSOOSCX,
VWF B IVTS V CBKIO WEO OE CSVF OISY.

—HBPPBVY QVMPJWSC

358   CSP RPZ CJ PKPEZCSAGH AV
LNCAPGDP. ZJI HPC CSP DSADRPG QZ
SNCDSAGH CSP PHH, GJC QZ VYNVSAGH
AC.   —NEGJXM S. HXNVJO

• • • • • • • • • • • • • • • • • •

359   NEQZA DBQY GCJ ZSQ ZYLSG ZYH
GCJ DTKK UZAQ MBQ VQNM NEQQFB
GCJ DTKK QIQS SQLSQM.

                    —ZUVSCNQ VTQSFQ

• • • • • • • • • • • • • • • • • •

360   WSNU GEQ XEBU RP GUERSRA. PJ
UBUR DPJMU, SI GEQ XEBU E GUERSRA
PN DXSHX S VSMEKKJPBU.

                    —EMXWUSAX FJSWWSERI

361   GQOT BOHBWO PJE LO DA D QPYO
PTX JBPSO FQPTRO, D KOWW KQOL D
QPYO DK PK QHLO DT LX JBPSO
GPWWOK.   —TDFE PSTOKKO

• • • • • • • • • • • • • • • • • •

362   D'AA ODFC KPV GJ DSCG PX ETGM
ZDJS PX OVK TC EGR. RGDJM XUGJYDR
EPVAS TGFC QVJYTCS TDN DJ MTC
NPVMT.   —OCJC QCUUCM

• • • • • • • • • • • • • • • • • •

363   DH ZED PTFF ZEVO E SXOEQ FOEROX
PMH PEDQB QH RH TQ EFF MTZBOFC HX
SOQ EFF QMO UXORTQ CHX RHTDS TQ.
                          —EDRXOP UEXDOSTO

364   JYN DFFQM G'LF HFFB ZFAAGBT VGX

BYZ ZY HWI SBIZVGBT JYN XI HGNZVKSI,

SBK VF MZGAA JYNTYZ ZY HNGBT XF

MYXFZVGBT.   —ZSBIS BYF

• • • • • • • • • • • • • • • • •

365   VYR E ZEJR-VA SEPTR GKSC

RHRUISCKQD XTNYR ES CEQL EQL LNQ'S

UVYC; NSCRUGKYR INV'TT TNNJ TKJR E

AESXCGNUJ FVKTS.   —TVXKTTR PETT

• • • • • • • • • • • • • • • • •

366   YGQ KGPL QLBKGO, B VGH GY

MGVVAUGGW ZCT KMGHK BQL FIQCGIK

HG KLL MGU HMLA'W ZL WQBUO UCHM

ZIVTCOT LALK BOW OG FMCO.

                              —PBHH TQGLOCOT

367   RZVKV BKV FY DFFYWVFR
XQARBFPVKA. NZBR NVKV RZVQ PYDFE
RZVKV DF RZV UDKAR CGBWV?

—NDGGDBO A. XTKKYTEZA

• • • • • • • • • • • • • • • • •

368   N DNHK SKIUI DEH E WMPQ PM SKI
SB SP STUM TX SKI NMSIRRNZIMVI.
SKIUI'H E WMPQ VERRIG "QUNZKSMIHH,"
QTS NS GPIHM'S DPUW.   —ZERREZKIU

• • • • • • • • • • • • • • • • •

369   CBADT J FWZJD AX J SBPPACIG
VAMMARNIS SPJVB, XADRB AS RWDXAXSX
QPADRAQJIIG WM VBJIADT FASO ZBD.

—KWXBQO RWDPJV

370   R HMB ZYRQVYJ R SMG CXHYTXZG,
IYUJYWYUREQY, REH ZM ZDUE RUMDEH
ZVUYY ZXNYJ SYCMUY TGXEB HMLE.

—UMSYUZ SYEQVTYG

• • • • • • • • • • • • • • • • •

371   AJ SKHTGDQ VFGRBVINNJ PGQBR
BKIHZ F MFJ, JKI UFJ PCPDRIFNNJ QPR
RK AP F AKZZ FDM SKHT RSPNCP BKIHZ
F MFJ.   —HKAPHR VHKZR

• • • • • • • • • • • • • • • • •

372   NXC TCAETUCT RECG HEN
SHRCTGNQHR NXQN JCEJMC BESMR
TQNXCT PC BTEHV QHR KEUAETNQPMC
NXQH TOVXN OH FQOM.

—AOHMCW JCNCT RSHHC

373   LHLC ZMRXMWXH NDRX LW EZUFW

FZTJW, DMX DE WJX TUXLWXFW NLGDU-

FLRZMT CLYJZMXF WJX SDUNH XRXU FLS.

—BDFJ GZNNZMTF

• • • • • • • • • • • • • • • • •

374   YSRTR XTR CVTR CRG YSXG PVCRG

AG CRGYXM SVZLAYXMZ—PSAES IWZY

DVRZ YV ZSVP PSV'Z QTAFAGD PSV

ETXOH.   —LRYRT FRXMR

• • • • • • • • • • • • • • • • •

375   CSM OMQFFR KOVDSCMZVZD CSVZD

QYJNC TVBBFM QDM VG CSM EZJHFMBDM

CSQC RJN'FF DOJH JNC JK VC.

—BJOVG BQR

376   QR QCUPAG WBA EVA OPDJ EVAR

GVCS PD MBPGCDG WDJ CD

WPBMIWDAG KALWNGA DCKCJR LWD

IAWUA.   —KNBE BARDCIJG

• • • • • • • • • • • • • • • • • •

377   JBGYBWBGULPB KY RCB CUGI XFGA

EFV IF UNRBG EFV HBR RKGBI FN IFKLH

RCB CUGI XFGA EFV UQGBUIE IKI.

                —LBXR HKLHGKPC

• • • • • • • • • • • • • • • • • •

378   ZLV'GY MLN NL WY GYDZ BSDYXVC

OX ZLV HLU'N AULR RFYDY ZLV'DY

MLOUM, WYBSVTY ZLV POMFN ULN MYN

NFYDY.   —ZLMO WYDDS

379   UW RQTRBY DG U LUW VZF ZUG

LUJR UNN YZR LDGYUXRG VZDPZ PUW

HR LUJR DW U ORBS WUBBFV ADRNJ.

                              —WDRNG HFZB

• • • • • • • • • • • • • • • • • •

380   T DOBZ O SXU XP DXJZF, NQU T

GXJ'U VOJU UX UOSB ONXQU UWOU.

T VXYB MZYF WOYG OJG T'D VXYUW

ZMZYF AZJU.   —JOXDT AODKNZSS

• • • • • • • • • • • • • • • • • •

381   GM NESY HYAYI CEYR FQPXW JYI

FDY. RJY KXRW WYCCR YAYIMPHY RJY'R

FR PCL FR E FG. WJYH RJY CEYR FQPXW

GM FDY.   —IPQYIW PIQYH

382   EOB GBACWY YJQ CL J YDBE DG
JMZJQG BJGDBI EOJW EOB LDIGE. SQ
EOB GBACWY YJQ QCT'IB CLL DE.

—XJAFDB VMBJGCW

• • • • • • • • • • • • • • • • •

383   FK'P TFPUXNVGMFHM KX KQFHI QXE
ZGHA OYXODY GVY PQXUIYT LA
QXHYPKA, GHT QXE JYE LA TYUYFK.

—HXYD UXEGVT

• • • • • • • • • • • • • • • • •

384   BE BCDVFQ MVF IWABRI BPFCD VYI
FME PFFRI YI BUTFID BI PBO BI B TFDVAQ
MVF DBURI BPFCD VAQ FME JVYUOQAE.

—PAEGBTYE OYIQBAUY

385   LA P QAQLRRX TF ENZB P ELBV
VF UZV CPT FJ AFGZFBZ ENFAZ
KFBHZCALVPFB SFCZA GZ, P WCZVZBT
VF LUCZZ.   —LRSZCV KLGQA

• • • • • • • • • • • • • • • • •

386   ZXZ-SXXQH DTFZQ FD'H HFPPV DX
FZAJHD DIX TXRCH' IXCQ FZ DIX KFZRDJH'
JZMXVKJZD; GRD FY SXXQFZW FH
JAOZJHSJZD, HX FH DTJ GOPPJD.

                        —MRPFO STFPL

• • • • • • • • • • • • • • • • •

387   FBA IAZF SANZEHA PQ N SNT'Z
BPTAZFJ LZT'F BLZ LTDPSA FNM HAFEHT.
LF'Z FBA YAHP NUCEZF PT BLZ INFBHPPS
ZDNGA.   —NHFBEH D. DGNHXA

388   MLDR NKFNTONDHN EYI ZYJREZ XN

ZEYZ OD NDRMYDS DLCLSU RLNI ZL ZEN

ZENYZNT JDMNII EN LT IEN EYI

CTLDHEOZOI.   —GYXNI YRYZN

• • • • • • • • • • • • • • • • •

389   DMYPW JNMTYKMPL YT QYHM

NXPPYPW F EMUMLMNV; VAX'ZM WAL

F QAL AI JMAJQM XPKMN VAX FPK

PADAKV'T QYTLMPYPW.   —DYQQ EQYPLAP

• • • • • • • • • • • • • • • • •

390   FDBE NXE QWGV XRWLXGN JRGE

XFFXTA QDBR FDBE'MB TJMRBMBV. W

NKCCJNB FDXF'N QDE LE PJGVHWND

QXN NJ TXGL QDBR W HGKNDBV DWL.

                —QWGG PWGGBNCWB

391   K AUWFGI TWJ JDGO AW NFHU

DVWFJ NRAMGB KB JUMSM XMSM

DTRVWIR MGAM XUWN K OTMX DA

XMGG.   —UMTSR IDZKI JUWSMDF

* * * * * * * * * * * * * * * * *

392   AWF AWOMQ TOAW SDFAFMKOMQ

XJI'DF OM Y QJJK UJJK OH AWYA

HJUFAOUFH XJI RYM YRAIYNNX ADORV

XJIDHFNC OMAJ CFFNOMQ EFAAFD.

               —RWYDNFH KF NOMA

* * * * * * * * * * * * * * * * *

393   G MV QLNLHVGOLQ VZ BEGTQHLO

JL JHAICEN ID GO NELGH RMNELH'F

HLTGCGAO, GR NELZ BMO RGOQ AIN

SEMN GN GF.   —BEMHTLF TMVJ

394   FUNM SJ YTH CNHBYHJY YTSPC SP
YTH FUNIK. JU FH JTUQIK JBEH JUWH UZ
SY ZUN YUWUNNUF.   —KUP THNUIK

• • • • • • • • • • • • • • • • • •

395   R SZH CE Z QZDL YLTLEDIU, ZEQ DBL
MWU DCCA FL BCYHLGZTA YRQREM.
DBZD SZH AREQ CX XWE, WEDRI SL YZE
CWD CX VWZYDLYH.

                        —HWHRL ICWTAH

• • • • • • • • • • • • • • • • • •

396   T OMXLPLNI TPPLPKEI JLSS RMP
XMSNI TSS CMKB OBMYSIVX, YKP LP JLSS
TRRMC IRMKZF OIMOSI PM VTAI LP JMBPF
PFI IGGMBP.   —FIBV TSYBLZFP

397   ZDX VTZMFHZX OJHT JL ZDX
XIVQHZMJKHT GCGZXF MG ZJ GDMLZ
ZJ ZDX MKIMWMIVHT ZDX NVAIXK JL
UVAGVMKO DMG XIVQHZMJK.

—PJDK OHAIKXA

• • • • • • • • • • • • • • • • •

398   YJTA BJTE XOGG BJT SZGG LA BJT
CTAOBT, BJT CTAOBZSC WZ AZB IAZY
YJTBJTS BZ OACYTS "KSTCTAB" ZS "AZB
VQLGBE."   —BJTZWZST SZZCTRTGB

• • • • • • • • • • • • • • • • •

399   FCRFRIMB INSFYNGNMB HPD GRCS:
ERK SLWE SRAMX BNB XRL SPQM YPIH
XMPC? SPNY NH NA.

—IHPAHRA BMYPFYPAM

400   M'X HCC MT DHBJQ JD WRRNMTL

YHTLRQJEV ARHNJTV JEK JD KZR ZHTYV

JD DJJCV. CRK'V VKHQK AMKZ

KPNRAQMKRQV.   —VJCJXJT VZJQK

• • • • • • • • • • • • • • • •

401   E SKEQLSA OEQK ERVQL HUMK

TUDGVOKG KETS AKEM UDK EDR E SEQY

LZOKG SZG UXD XKZFSL ZD ULSKM

NKUNQK'G NELZKDTK.   —PUSD VNRZCK

• • • • • • • • • • • • • • • •

402   VSVZF IWB PWK W ZOTPQ QA

DQQVZ XPWQ PV QPOBJK QZDQP, WBR

VSVZF AQPVZ IWB PWK W ZOTPQ QA

JBAEJ POI RAXB GAZ OQ.

                    —KWIDVY MAPBKAB

403   EGN TYEYON, RPPFOUSHQ EF VFZN

VPSNHESVEV, LSAA IN NDRPEAX ASBN

EGN JRVE, FHAX TRO ZFON NDJNHVSMN.

—KFGH EGFZRV VARUNB

. . . .

404   MRX NXOLVS IRK LV JXI WVVA PVVFL

ONX INHMMXS HL MROM LV JXI CXVCYX

IRV EOS INHMX FSVI OSKMRHSW.

—IOYMXN POWXRVM

. . . .

405   WL AHI PQFX AHIY BJWGSYKF XH

WRMYHEK, GKX XJKR HEKYJKQY XJK

FWBK XJWFDU AHI UQA QTHIX XJKR XH

HXJKYU.   —JQWR DWFHXX

406 EOWOA KFAAT SZFJQ QPO HXNO FL

TFJA VPAXHQCSH QAOO. XE QPO OTOH

FL VPXIBAOE, QPOT SAO SII QPXAQT

LOOQ QSII.   —ISAAT KXIBO

• • • • • • • • • • • • • • • • •

407 DJIGZ UZC LURF DNHH CJ UF RMGB

OHGUFG, UZC IGZ UZC CJAF FMJQHC

VGHUY UZC AGR QFGC RJ RMG NCGU.

                    —VJKGVR U. MGNZHGNZ

• • • • • • • • • • • • • • • • •

408 WZU VMH OK ZOGH V CZVBH

TZFOBM LQDWAMQ V KLWDI. WBXH

FWA'DH VEWVDU, LQHDH'K BWLQOBM

FWA XVB UW VEWAL OL.

                    —MWZUV IHOD

409   NJDCDNDPB, YDSR JUDL, PQXKYO HR TRLCYR RLXKTQ CX LXKJDPQ U BUL'P TJXECQ EDCQXKC ORPCJXADLT QDP JXXCP.   —WJULS U. NYUJS

• • • • • • • • • • • • • • • • • •

410   HCREXVZVPA FK I YIA VG VMPIXFUFXP HEC BXFJCMKC KV HEIH NIX LVCKX'H EIJC HV CODCMFCXRC FH.

—NIO GMFKRE

• • • • • • • • • • • • • • • • • •

411   OKMMVXF DVUX WXKELXJ SBX VBPKDZKCDX DXJJSB: WS WLVBH SU WLVBAJ UKM XBSZAL KLXKF BSW WS JKR WLXO.

—IXUUXMJSB OKELKOXM

412   EH TDMW TDQ BTXMS RQMM RNXQ
MTLQ HNTP HFMCQ MTLQ FC TDQ BFD
RQMM PXCVNTTPC HNTP RTFSCRTTMC.

—GFRVFNEDQ PFDCHEQMS

• • • • • • • • • • • • • • • • • •

413   NIRMQTWTFUREW HOTFOICC MEC
SIOIWZ HOTPUVIV JC DUNM STOI
IBBURUIQN SIEQC BTO FTUQF
LERYDEOVC.   —EWVTJC MJKWIZ

• • • • • • • • • • • • • • • • • •

414   MPJAVYM JXF VW XVNB ZBVYM
VYSPBOWVYMXC KBYOXVDBF LJP O
SPVUB CJE GOQBY'I SJUUVIIBF.

—OYIGJYC KJABXX

415   WP GWPU LUEU AMJB, LU LVMGZ CU

CVEF VGZ XFZ XRYWUSU KVMBY XCVMB

BYU BWIU LU'Z JXSUZ UFVMOY BV UFAVK

WB.   —AWI PWUCWO

• • • • • • • • • • • • • • • • •

416   USIVKSV KWKUXKCUXUVE OUVZLGV

HLSIVKSV QJAIASHA UI QJLCKCXE VZA

CAIV JLXA K FLVZAJ HKS QXKE.

                            —XLVVA CKUXES

• • • • • • • • • • • • • • • • •

417   SOPXZM EPO ECJEZO: PO XIZV

FRAOY YCGGOYY DPOI PO YEWGAY

PWY IOGA XCE.

                        —HRFOY SJVRIE GXIRIE

418   BFT PZQI TZL VRWQ OD KZJPI

FVZTQ, PQIXRLQ LGQ EFML LGFL

IZBQLRBQI GQ GFI LZ QFL LGQB.

—FPVFR ILQWQTIZT

•••••••••••••••••

419   ZCVGDGFGLJM BEC FCRZVLGJ

LOCKD DEI RIPGL LHI VGSI MLGVCHM

BEC FCRZVLGJ LOCKD DEI MIL.

—IJCFE ZCBIVV

•••••••••••••••••

420   D VX YLP V SBRBPVNDVY FBEVWOB

D QLSB VYDXVQO; D VX V SBRBPVNDVY

FBEVWOB D GVPB UQVYPO.

—V. AGDPYBC FNLAY

421   LKIGB SHI'Z PFB BKF UHTTYIGEE, PFZ
YZ SHI PFB BKF H BHSUZ PYW GIKFWU ZK
TFXX FT DYWUZ HXKIWEYJG YZ.

—JHRYJ XGG DKZU

* * * * * * * * * * * * * * * * * *

422   ICC VIKKXIZWE IKW LIFFS. XN'E
NKSXBZ NQ CXDW NQZWNLWK
IJNWKAIKGE NLIN MITEWE ICC NLW
FKQOCWVE.   —ELWCCWS AXBNWKE

* * * * * * * * * * * * * * * * *

423   BR CBUC BUG KA LAAIG, WKUXRG,
KAT ZRQQUTG SK BSG LUESIJ OUG
ZRQAC ZJ U LIUGB AL ISQBCKSKQ.

—CBAEUG LMIIRT

424   PZAAXFZZU CK V GAVTS FPSIS EPSX
GAVTS XZJ JDUSI TZDEIVTE CDKESVU ZN
JDUSI ZYKSIHVECZD.

—FVAESI FCDTPSAA

• • • • • • • • • • • • • • • • •

425   O QUFL IOXMBFLKLI WQUW UHH
QSRUP LFOH MBRLX AKBR WQOX: RUP'X
NLOPY SPUNHL WB XOW XWOHH OP U
KBBR.   —NHUOXL ZUXMUH

• • • • • • • • • • • • • • • • •

426   DXTTGDP RG NB N'R KTXLA, HOP
UZVL'P PUG BNLG YNLG HGPKGGL VZLNPE
ZLS RZSLGVV AXPPGL BNLGT?

—AGXTAG WTNDG

427   YB QBI VBQYTEQ ILT ASYJETQI BU
NQBILTD CTVNSRT GI YGUUTDR UDBE
HBSD BKQ. HBS ENH CBIL CT KDBQJ.

—YNQYTEGR

• • • • • • • • • • • • • • • • •

428   CYGC ZK CXH YTC RW OYDZJS
SAHKCK WHHE YC XROH PXHJ CXYC'K
THYEEV PXHTH VRA PZKX CXHV PHTH.

—SHRTSH H. IHTSOYJ

• • • • • • • • • • • • • • • • •

429   ON XSAQA'M BTFVTA GOMXATOTD
XV LSVY O VLA YVTAF, O'Y CQACBQAZ XV
NVQDAX OX ON FVK BQA.

—AQQVG NGFTT

430   MYV DVMMVS XV KVVF WDRBM
RBSTVFQVT, MYV KVXVS MUEVT XV YWQV
MR PHRZP TREVDRJL VFTV JRXH MR KVVF
MWFF.   —RJVMMW

• • • • • • • • • • • • • • • • •

431   CY AUP XZWRX WKWZA TCXPRXCUG
RT R SCYW-RGB-BWRXD ORXXWZ, AUP'SS
BCW R SUX UY XCOWT.

                         —BWRG TOCXD

• • • • • • • • • • • • • • • • •

432   WM DUOBP JRKBCWUO YROR
GWDAPQ MUPPUYWXN OSPRG, YR TUSPI
AOUNOBD B TUDASFRO FU JR DUOBP.

                         —GBDSRP A. NWXIRO

433   SXNWN ICGS ON GUINSXJAQ SU
ZHCVCAHSCWN—ZDSNW ZRR, EUC
ANLNW GNN ZAE GJHT VUWHCVJANG.

—OUO QUMMZWM

• • • • • • • • • • • • • • • • •

434   NABHGA PHCY JAHJEA CYUGY
NHUCYXID UNHRY YWAXG BUPXEZ YGAA,
YWAZ RCRUEEZ MH U DHHM JGRIXID
VHN.   —H.U. NUYYXCYU

• • • • • • • • • • • • • • • • •

435   BZPZOW DYXX LHLT DYB SNL PUSSXL
ZM SNL ELVLE. SNLTL'E SZZ AIQN
MTUSLTBYRYBJ DYSN SNL LBLAW.

—NLBTW FYEEYBJLT

436   WJBC KENT IQJ CERTD IQJ'ON

VSYFJYCNF GSQH CEN BZEQQM QG

NAUNSRNTZN, BQHNQTN CERTDB JU

Y TNK ZQJSBN.   —HYSI E. KYMFSRU

• • • • • • • • • • • • • • • • • •

437   N XOSL JNGECSLYLJ ZXL OYZ CU

JLELNSNBI JNMHCVOZG. N ZLHH ZXLV

ZXL ZYWZX OBJ ZXLF BLSLY TLHNLSL VL.

—EOVNHHC JN EOSCWY

• • • • • • • • • • • • • • • • • •

438   GLV SKG QFDOE DQ'P K YLOU HKG

JLHO QFX TLKJ QL QFX JTVU PQLTX, MVQ

QFKQ'P WVPQ ZXKOVQP QL PZKRX.

—JLVUYKP KJKSP

439   ZCDZOC XBD TVFC BKRPDQL FIDX
IDPBKIU VMDNP BKRPDQL. LDN WVI RCC
PBVP KI PBC RDQP DS BKRPDQL PBCL
TVFC.   —U.F. WBCRPCQPDI

• • • • • • • • • • • • • • • • •

440   KJUNIJ O ENS AGIIOJR, O CGR MOD
SCJNIOJM GKNWS KIOVEOVE WH
FCOPRIJV; VNQ O CGBJ MOD FCOPRIJV
GVR VN SCJNIOJM.   —ZNCV QOPANS

• • • • • • • • • • • • • • • • •

441   M OML IUT SNQIW CUQ ITEPJ CUQ
WMOQ MC YNYCX MW UQ JNJ MC
CIQLCX UMW IMWCQJ CUNECX XQMEW
TY UNW PNYQ.   —OFUMOOMJ MPN

442   SV Y PORROJ-XJAOJOA UXJQA, RMO
LZEGZ TXRM UXFQA GMXU FE SV XIRXPOJ
YVA OYR RMO QOYKOG YNROJ RMOZ'KO
NYQQOV.   —OAUYJA GROKOVGXV

• • • • • • • • • • • • • • • • •

443   GNS ZAAKDWZSKQQU DBVGRQN ZS
BCN BPVBC, RVB GZDB ZL BCNG EWAI
BCNGDNQMND VE KSX CVPPU ZLL KD WL
SZBCWSJ CKX CKEENSNX.

                    —FWSDBZS ACVPACWQQ

• • • • • • • • • • • • • • • • •

444   DGXAWIHRMJGX, ONJDN JH
HQBBGHWK MG SW R MOG-ORT
HMIWWM, JH MIWRMWK ST URXT RH
JY JM OWIW R KJAJKWK NJVNORT.

                    —UJHH URXXWIH

445   XRFVYKJL RZPJ LJPJK SJJL PJKW

NMMY ZB VFABJLFLN BM BRJFK JVYJKA,

SQB BRJW RZPJ LJPJK DZFVJY BM FUFBZBJ

BRJU.   —CZUJA SZVYEFL

• • • • • • • • • • • • • • • • •

446   NJHEQ DK H ZJWB NSTT, NWJHWB

HIIHDW, HGN RB HNZDLJ EU BUS DK EU

QHZJ GUEQDGY PQHEJZJW EU NU PDEQ

DE.   —P. KURJWKJE RHSYQHR

• • • • • • • • • • • • • • • • •

447   AC GXNJC IEXYCWQCY IL IEX

USNWNRT RI VCR U GNFFU RI IEX JIIX

OUYRCX RKUL UL UDSEWULHC.

                          —ANWW JEXYR

448   E GYRHZERHG VYPJHO ES ZNH

RQPBSQIZBOHOG YS SYYAWOYYS EZHRG

THHW Q SYYA YO ZVY YP ZNHEO

WQFOYAA ZY ZHGZ ZNEPCG.

—QAQP IYOHP

• • • • • • • • • • • • • • • • •

449   AR UYGEFP QD RDI EL TPQ AUXXEPY:

EM RDI MEHY U TDDY SEMP RDI'OO CP

JUWWR; EM HDQ, RDI SEOO CPFDAP U

WJEODLDWJPX.   —LDFXUQPL

• • • • • • • • • • • • • • • • •

450   KR UWFH JLHZV NZVZUVLWISH KU

QWV ZQQWGQNHX HPHLM FWLQKQJ, YH

RHHT Z NHLVZKQ PWKX. QWVSKQJ KQ

VSH IZIHL VWXZM, YH UKJS.

—TWLX ZNVWQ

451   QVZ FZIP TYP RDCVWCYO PV ALCY
LD RFKLJP. DV VDY RI RFKMYIIYO GRPA
PAY GVD-WVIP MYJVMO VU PAY
MYUYMYY.   —XVAD A. AVWJVFH

452   QE QL G HOZGE SZTX YDO G AGW
ED CZ QW TDNZ MQES SQALZTY. YDO
GW GREDO, SDMZNZO, QE QL
GCLDTJEZTI ZLLZWEQGT.

                      —ODCZOE ADOTZI

453   UOXZX JZX UOZXX EUJPXE CS KJW:
OX HXRTXAXE TW EJWUJ NRJME, OX
QCXE WCU HXRTXAX TW EJWUJ NRJME,
OX TE EJWUJ NRJME.   —HCH DOTRRTDE

454   IUH IARGYDH PFIU IHDDFWK Q KRRN

JIRAV FJ IUQI FI FWMQAFQYDV AHXFWNJ

IUH RIUHA EHDDRP RE Q NGDD RWH.

—JFN SQHJQA

• • • • • • • • • • • • • • • • •

455   BRAAVJB KJ VERK HQZTIE LR IVOR

HVAAVJB ZJ K MVJ. VA HQZTIE CKOR PZT

WTCM TM KJE EZ HZCRAQVJB.

—R.I. HVCMHZJ

• • • • • • • • • • • • • • • • •

456   JM GME DMVVU TOMRE UMRV

WVMONPIC DZEA ITEAPITEZKC; Z TCCRVP

UMR IZGP TVP BTV SVPTEPV.

—TNOPVE PZGCEPZG

457   WA WF HOART YIGC AH

CWFAWTXZWFY VRALRRT AYR BTHMBF HO

EWOR ITC AYHFR HO HNNHGAZTWAQ.

—OGRCRGWMB NYWEEWNF

• • • • • • • • • • • • • • • • •

458   CGGCFVQWZVO ZI EZIINX HO ECIV

GNCGUN HNBDQIN ZV ZI XFNIINX ZW

CYNFDUUI DWX UCCRI UZRN LCFR.

—VMCEDI NXZICW

• • • • • • • • • • • • • • • • •

459   ZWM YGXI ZWNGS ZWLZ

VYGZNGKMA ZY SNTM KA UYJM CYJ YKJ

UYGMI NA ZWM DMNSWNGS ULVWNGM.

—SMYJSM VXLJO

460   OEIJ, WLDJRSZGDH, LJZHJTV SE REV
PRDVJ HJEHOJ NZ KPTG NZ N TEKKER
GNVLJS WEL ZEKJVGDRY.

—NRVER TGJQGEI

. . . .

461   KJW SEQRK XEXWVK HEQ CV
CKJWMRK MR SJWV JW HWWNR
LQCKWHDN CVO JCR VE EVW KE KJCVF.

—SWVOG SCQO

. . . .

462   LG SWMLOLZQ, LC EWH IDGO
DGEONLGX QDLF, DQV D KDG; LC EWH
IDGO DGEONLGX FWGJ, DQV D IWKDG.

—KDPXDPJO ONDOZNJP

463   APM LBFEMEA AF QMGTMLAVFR I
QMGEFR MXMG LFHME VE NPMR PM
TVBBE FZA I KFO IQQBVLIAVFR TFGH.

               —EAIRBMC K. GIRSIBB

• • • • • • • • • • • • • • • • •

464   JD RIFVIE VIYR JO VI HVIC QMUAZN
AZVAJMVO RAZZOEH SIE SIWE. WZYOHH
VQOEO MEO VQEOO IVQOE COICYO.

               —IEHIZ LOYYOH

• • • • • • • • • • • • • • • • •

465   GH'T B ZSMSTTGPW ALSW IPCZ
WSGDLEPZ UPTST LGT KPE; GH'T B
RSXZSTTGPW ALSW IPC UPTS IPCZ PAW.

               —LBZZI T. HZCFBW

466   R NWJRS XRYK TJHTBJ SCZYD SCJK

RWJ SCZYDZYN QCJY SCJK RWJ XJWJBK

WJRWWRYNZYN SCJZW TWJAMOZPJL.

—QZBBZRX ARXJL

467   B XALBE RV UROK B HKB SBM—JAF

WBE'H HKUU PAX VHQAEM VPK RV FEHRU

JAF IFH PKQ RE PAH XBHKQ.

—EBEWJ QKBMBE

468   VUPQBTCZJN XZUBRI SR KP ZER

HUJR, VTZ GPR ZEGTYEZ QRCZ SR JUOS;

XGGP K'I VR ZGG CGGB ZG PRRI UP

UPZK-ZERHZ UOUBS.   —YKPU BGZEHROX

469   G YQUVRO AOQAYO XRQ HOOA
TQDC. VROI ULO EQXULTC XRQ RUWOK'V
DQV VRO DFVC VQ PGVO AOQAYO
VROJCOYWOC.

—UFDFCV CVLGKTPOLD

• • • • • • • • • • • • • • • • •

470   P MPYF RJIJWPZPBY WJDK
JFHXGRPYU. JWJDK RPNJ ZBNJEBFK RHDYZ
BY RSJ ZJR, P UB PYRB RSJ BRSJD DBBN
GYF DJGF G EBBV.   —UDBHXSB NGDO

• • • • • • • • • • • • • • • • •

471   UQHM KQAROMU ZCNQDKM
SMKPAUM QG P HCUALZMDUVPLZCLT;
QVIMDU, SMKPAUM VIMB ALZMDUVPLZ
MPKI QVIMD VQQ JMOO.

—MNPL MUPD

472   HPGBG VN WRAO WRG
EVYYGBGRXG KGHJGGR Z QZEQZR ZRE
QG. HPG QZEQZR HPVRCN PG VN NZRG.
V CRWJ V ZQ QZE.   —NZASZEWB EZAV

• • • • • • • • • • • • • • • • •

473   SPUHXLMM OM SPUWOUKBDDN
BQQPOUWOUH GBSW-GOUZOUH
SPVVOWWLLM, CRLU CRBW CL XLBDDN
ULLZ BXL MPVL GBSW-GBSOUH
SPVVOWWLLM.   —XPHLX BDDLU

• • • • • • • • • • • • • • • • •

474   JQWAWPY WD AOU VPST
RQVIUDDWVP JOUQU PV VPU
HVPDWNUQD TVB QWNWHBSVBD
WI TVB UEQP PV KVPUT.

                      —MBSUD QUPEQN

475   PWZXIO PI XIKYRLBIM RBRLBC QE
KQIOCBWW MQ GQMB EQC MBCR
JXRXMW XW JXZB PWZXIO P KTXKZBI
MQ GQMB EQC KQJQIBJ WPIHBCW.

—LQL XIOJXW

• • • • • • • • • • • • • • • • • •

476   OY TLX SNOZJ RLKH BQZ'S BLXZS,
SPT VXSSOZK SNPUU RLK AOHBXOSH OZ
TLXP VLBJUS QZR SNUZ KOCOZK YORL
LZWT SML LY SNUG.   —VNOW VQHSLPUS

• • • • • • • • • • • • • • • • • •

477   M GDZ'W HYJ DOBH GYH Y WDOCR
HURDDN, KOW GX RYE DOB DGZ
UDBDZXB. GX OHXE WD GBMWX XHHYJH
NMVX "GRYW M'S CDMZC WD KX MI M
CBDG OF."   —NXZZJ KBOUX

478   ZOVMFAJK WVOFAER VMLU MJZ
VYVOS GJV GQ XR EG IV NXAVEBS MJZ
RMQVBS AJRMJV VYVOS JAKUE GQ GXO
BAYVR.   —DABBAMF ZVFVJE

• • • • • • • • • • • • • • • • •

479   GO GJ ECDZO OH MD Z MQHTAD.
VGOP QHV DSXDLOZOGHTJ GO'J RDCU
DZJU OH JWCXCGJD XDHXQD.
                         —XZKDQZ ZTADCJHT

• • • • • • • • • • • • • • • • •

480   NCD NBK QDOYWPH TDAWGDF UKT
FRAADFF OTD XRWQYWPH O XDNNDT
LKRFDNTOG OPY UWPYWPH O XWHHDT
QKKGCKQD.   —DYHOT O. FACKOUU

481   QBCCYM JPM BA GJNBWP J HGKBHM
RMIXMMW IXK IMQOIJIBKWA JWC
HGKKABWP IGM KWM IGJI'YY PMI EKV
GKQM MJLYBML.   —CJW RMWWMII

• • • • • • • • • • • • • • • • • •

482   OV NCGNAC ZCKAAS AODCE PG
XGZD, XC'E IPOAA RC NAGXOBL PQC
AKBE XOPQ IPOUDI KBE PZKBINGZPOBL
LGGEI GB GHZ RKUDI.

                        —XOAAOKY VCKPQCZ

• • • • • • • • • • • • • • • • • •

483   Y ZXV'W NOAD QEOW GXT UOG
OIXTW SD, OU RXVC OU GXT UOG
UXSDWEYVC OIXTW SD, OVZ OU RXVC
OU GXT UFDRR SG VOSD AYCEW.

                        —CDXACD S. NXEOV

484   GAQ CLKQ GY DJRNGA IGCQ
NIMGCRDAR RODA DKK GROQCE
JGAENERE NA AQSQC BGNAU
DAHRONAU RODR EGIQGAQ QKEQ
JDA BG YGC HGL.   —JDKSNA JGGKNBUQ

• • • • • • • • • • • • • • • • •

485   R LJS'D YRQQ IQRKB TGD R QRYK DJ
XKBB FRDZ DZKRV XRSLB. R ZJQL DZKX
ETJPK NQJTKB. DZKO IVKEY JGD ESL
OKQQ, "FZJE, R'X FEO DJJ ZRNZ!"

                              —TVGHK TEGX

• • • • • • • • • • • • • • • • •

486   PJR XRYBPE AL JYKWIC Y OAU
WIHAFR WT PJYP PJRGR WT IAP RIABCJ
FAIRE PA XBE UJYP EAB QAI'P GRYOOE
IRRQ.   —GYE WIFYI

487   NKLGT HKFRGSN JB GCKFOKFI

JB VFT OKFY KN ZJRFY GJ MSVY GJ

AJFBRNKJF VFY RFCVWWKFSNN.

—XVHSN GCREZSE

• • • • • • • • • • • • • • • • • •

488   PNZGZ'E DVPNODS JGVDS JOPN

EVMPNZGD XTKOBVGDOT PNTP T GOEZ

OD PNZ VXZTD KZYZK JVMKCD'P XMGZ.

—GVEE RTXCVDTKC

• • • • • • • • • • • • • • • • • •

489   K'N DAZEUILWG BZJVT JR AXL

YZKUFWLD K XEQL. YXEA K'N IKQKUI

VB KU LWEDAKOKAG, K'N IEKUKUI KU

YKDTJN.   —DVCEUUL DJNLZD

490   QMVY BRIBGR LI ORMCTL FGIXRL

LIIHX CX FRHYVCTGK TIY JK FITFRHT

DTGRXX C'J ORMCTL YMRHR QCYM 'RJ.

—LIGGK BVHYIT

• • • • • • • • • • • • • • • • • •

491   RXIIJXHD JE ZJND X UJCZJT. XQBDI

BLD SDXWBJQWZ RWEJV JE CUDI, BLD

EBIJTHE XID EBJZZ XBBXVLDA.

—FXVCS SIXWAD

• • • • • • • • • • • • • • • • • •

492   EK JXXMKO GU WI EK EGO LKKS

ZXAFKO WSNX EWU DJXNEKU GSO EGO

IXFQXNNKS NX UGR "PEKS."

—Z.Q. PXOKEXAUK

493   X'DN HNDNA SNNH FNQKITV. HIY
NDNH OUNH BL PQP MXHXVUNP YUN
MXMYU CAQPN Q LNQA SNMIAN X PXP.

—FNMM MIJOIAYUL

• • • • • • • • • • • • • • • • •

494   WIY ABYNZXWI: XD ZQXN XN ZQY
XIDWLVEZXWI ETY, QWK GWVY IWHWMO
PIWKN EIOZQXIT?   —LWHYLZ VEIPWDD

• • • • • • • • • • • • • • • • •

495   AJD SVRJA AF UD JDMSC CFDO YFA
MXAFNMAVBMQQK VYBQXCD AJD SVRJA
AF UD AMLDY ODSVFXOQK.

—JXUDSA J. JXNGJSDK

496   RSJQQ W'UNWUD HM CNXCKM
RWW NCRQ WJ RWW QCJNK VWJ
CBKRSHBF KWG XCBR RW IW.

—ZQCB-YCGN MCJRJQ

• • • • • • • • • • • • • • • • •

497   UJ AMPL TQD Q DKMNTE
MUYLGMULVE MV TLI DYLLRT. LFLIJ VSA
QVG ETLV DTL DESYD ES ZILQETL.

—BMUUJ GXIQVEL

• • • • • • • • • • • • • • • • •

498   GYNLN'H KODM KON UZM GK YZPN
Z YZTTM IZLLVZEN, ZOW ZH HKKO ZH V
DNZLO UYZG VG VH V'DD ENG IZLLVNW
ZEZVO.   —QDVOG NZHGUKKW

499   UP ADUBPDB, LVB DQBZUL WJBA LJ
LVB EKP OVJ DJPTUPDBA LVB OJQMZ, PJL
LJ OVJE LVB UZBK XUQAL JDDSQA.

—AUQ XQKPDUA ZKQOUP

• • • • • • • • • • • • • • • • •

500   FKLTL LQBZFZ XU YUWBFBRBMX BX
BXVBM VMTBXI LXUJIK FU MFFLGYF FU
LQYWMBX FU FKL GMZZLZ FKMF RUHZ
RMX CL LMFLX.   —BXVBTM IMXVKB

• • • • • • • • • • • • • • • • •

501   X HDFCVQLTFZ NCWACCV
DCZRDWCD XVQ LRIDSC KXLWL RVKP
IVWFK FW FL ZDRHFWXNKC HRD RVC
WR NCWDXP WTC RWTCD.

—UXIDCCV QRAQ

502   IUMDADXDJQR JVC ICUIMC ZNU,
ZNCQ ANCE RCC MDLNA JA ANC CQG
US ANC AHQQCM, LU UHA JQG KHE
RUFC FUVC AHQQCM.   —PUNQ THDQAUQ

• • • • • • • • • • • • • • • • •

503   XDCWPWTWUJG UIH PVH GUAH UCC
DLHI. PVHO XIDAWGH PD SQWCB U
SIWBEH HLHJ MVHIH PVHIH WG JD IWLHI.
                    —JWFWPU FVIQGVTVHL

• • • • • • • • • • • • • • • • •

504   LW LY OSW ESPWC IO
LOWGDDLXGOW HIO'Y WLHG WS FG LO
WCG HIRSPLWT. FT JGULOLWLSO, WCGPG
IPG IDPGIJT GOSNXC QGSQDG WS JS
WCIW.   —X.C. CIPJT

505   EFQLGRP GQ LZP GIQFSDIRP YP ZDXP
UI UFS CGXPQ, DIB UMPBGPIRP GQ LZP
WSPNGFN YP WDH VUS GL.

—YGCCGDN WPII

• • • • • • • • • • • • • • • • •

506   BR BD I JIEUGSMOD RLBEU QMS I
EIRBMEIV PIEJBJIRG RM DIX RLBEUD RLIR
FGMFVG YBULR SGYGYCGS.

—GOUGEG YPPISRLX

• • • • • • • • • • • • • • • •

507   SP AXM NSC PSKL CA SXACZMY:
FKYCZLSUP SYM HKQM EVY FSHHP—CZM
JAYM UAV ZSGM, CZM JAYM UAV OSO.

—JSYHS JAYOSX

508   Z OSWZSPS IYRVWM ISVQVR XVR
TVES GNZC XYARGIK UNVG ZG YRXS UVC
... V WVIQS VIXGZX ISQZYR XYPSISM
UZGN ZXS.   —CGSPS TVIGZR

• • • • • • • • • • • • • • • • •

509   VZS KESGV VZDFK GHUBV
NSWUOEGOQ DX VZGV DV KDMSX
SMSEQ MUVSE G OZGFOS VU NU
XUWSVZDFK XVBJDN.   —GEV XJGFNSE

• • • • • • • • • • • • • • • • •

510   VUGYV ELTUCVL ZGQP DGEL M
FUYRFGPYFP GR ZGNP ATGXGYV OUCT
FMT DGEL ELP KTMNPR UY.
                              —KCAA RFLCZKPTV

511 TQCDEJDKYTGPW JU TA QAYJZTHNR
ZNPJIHN XDY CNHHJAK CPN CYQCP
TEDQC DCPNY GNDGHN.

—GPJHJG KQNRTHHT

• • • • • • • • • • • • • • • • •

512 ZYL PRYX ZYL QMJ DMYXGRD YWE
XTJR QWFYVB JAJMZBTGRD TLMBV, QRE
XTQB EYJV RYB TLMB EYJV RYB XYMP.

—TZ DQMERJM

• • • • • • • • • • • • • • • • •

513 XBUV ZLRS KSTBE TJ IRFO TYYVEYBLE
TJ ZLR CL ZLRS OTBS, TEC ZLR'QQ KV T
YOLRJTEC YBIVJ KVYYVS LMM.

—ITQFLQI A

514   YA RYZZYGU CEO DVM EGOCMB,
CM'K VEWM OPZWMK EZZ PIB XBPLZMHO
E ZPGU DYHM EUP.   —KYTR UBMUPBJ

• • • • • • • • • • • • • • • • •

515   GMXZSBT ZG KZVS E GBSR. ZQ TMA
NMF'B VSSU ZB GBZOOSN AU, TMA LSB E
KMB MQ GXAY MF BMU.

                    —SNREON EHHST

• • • • • • • • • • • • • • • •

516   XGTBZVVZ ETCKCXZ, AGTUQVI
PALXKVLPZH, NZLXK: C ELX'P YZVCZBZ
C SLCH XCXZPI-KCR HGVVLAK LXH C'N
KPCVV QTXUAI.   —NCMZ MLVCX

517   PFKOK EOK UXQL PSU TQEGGKG UB

MKZKGPOWEXG WX PFKGK ZELG UB

OKTDQKGG IUPUO POEBBWT—PFK

CHWTD EXZ PFK ZKEZ.

—PFUIEG OUJKOP ZKSEO

• • • • • • • • • • • • • • • • •

518   AT AZC JBBZVQJFZU YUZVATV JY

VQUTFBT KAZK HZCT AQV BJFMTGVZKQJF

OTGYTBKUW CTUQIAKYXU.

—VWCFTW VHQKA

• • • • • • • • • • • • • • • • •

519   W HDR'S NTJDZ QKO DRP KSUJO

XDOOWDYJ, MFS SUJ NJHOJS KQ KFO

XDOOWDYJ WN SUDS VJ UDAJ

DMNKCFSJCP RKSUWRY WR HKXXKR.

—XDXWJ JWNJRUKVJO

520   HGV HY LUV OVBBHGB HY USBLHKA

SB LUDL GHLUSGW SB HYLVG D WHHT

LUSGW LH TH DGT DOQDAB D JOVIVK

LUSGW LH BDA.   —QSOO TCKDGL

● ● ● ● ● ● ● ● ● ● ● ● ● ● ● ● ● ●

521   O HOR KXXCMGDU YGWE MCVTGX

KS KWEDS GHMKSWORW VCJGRDJJ

XORRKW, ORU RDDU RKW, OWWDRU WK

JMDTTGRQ.

            —ROMKTDKR VKROMOSWD

● ● ● ● ● ● ● ● ● ● ● ● ● ● ● ● ●

522   RW ASJXPEJVIDS'T J HBVVHD

ECSADVEGH, OGV ID HBQDT VC ABND RD

JPNBYD. CXD PJW, ID VCCQ RD JTBPD JXP

HDEV RD VIDSD.   —SCX SBYIJSPT

523   HXQ SMESKIQ KZ G UJFQEGU

QLMDGHJKB JI HK VGRQ PKM

SXJUKIKSXJDGU QBKMYX HK GDDQSH

HXQ ZGDH HXGH PKM TJUU BQAQE VGRQ

VMDX VKBQP.   —BKEVGB LKMYUGI

• • • • • • • • • • • • • • • • •

524   DI DP'V E GDTT, PRS KYVP YIIDOS

MDTT HSP DP PY LYJ DF PMSFPL-IYJW

RYJWV. DI DP'V E ORSOU, ETTYM PRSA E

OYJKTS MSSUV.   —WDOREWQ FSSQREA

• • • • • • • • • • • • • • • • •

525   Z XSZSDXSDVDZC DX XFGQFCQ YIF

DX NFFU ZS KDNJPQX WJS YIF UFQXC'S

IZAQ SIQ BQPXFCZEDST SF WQ ZC

ZVVFJCSZCS.   —PFT ITUQ

526   EBWD QC R SPRXD GBA ZMBJ AS
JRKNQKZ NB PDRLD, RKU ZMBJ BPU
JRKNQKZ NB ZDN HRXV NB.

—YBEK DU SQDMXD

• • • • • • • • • • • • • • • • •

527   KW NICJI BN DUPJ UW UEEHJ EKJ
RIND MGIUBGS, ONL DLMB RKIMB GIJUBJ
BSJ LWKAJIMJ.   —GUIH MUQUW

• • • • • • • • • • • • • • • • •

528   WUD KOZPWK OJLD PDTZPCK
ODZOSD'K JTTZGOSFKUGDVWK, WUD
NPZVW OJLD VZWUFVL MIW WUDFP
NJFSIPDK.   —EIKWFTD DJPS RJPPDV

529 ZHDW LHFTBWZ RH HCWA QKWPA
XFORWQZ CWAS LEAWYFBBS WCWAS
DHIQK; HQKWAZ NFZQ RH HCWA QKWD.

—ZEBBS THTBPI

• • • • • • • • • • • • • • • • •

530 TVMQDI UESKR QU CHZKEJM ELC
UZOC ELQDI ZU ISQDI ES Z KZUQDS,
SDJM PQEL DS KSKREZQJ UCGAQKC.

—ECB ZJJCD

• • • • • • • • • • • • • • • • •

531 RPA QOZX BAVHQO TPQ ZKHRAOH
RQ MQRP HKJAH QD YO YVFSGAOR KH
RPA DAZZQT KO RPA OAUR YBYVRGAOR.

—VSRP MVQTO

532   KLJVGKZ GH HL MDPCWWCHHGKZ
CH TCJSVGKZ HLDMLKM YL HLDMJVGKZ
JVCJ RLQ HCGY SLQUYK'J PM YLKM.

—HCD MTGKZ

. . . .

533   WRVROWRONW VXT JOUT V
GOUOZO. CAVR RATH XTDTVJ OW
WPMMTWRODT, GPR CAVR RATH NFZNTVJ
OW DORVJ.   —VVXFZ JTDTZWRTOZ

. . . .

534   LS HDKBSQ HRGBYXS HVKBGDXQK
DXVYFQ TVNQJRKL MVENK BV PDZS BLS
TVNQJRKL BLRFZ BLSA ESXS TVRFT
HNDGSK.   —JXSQ DNNSF

535   Z CVZMM CWJ W ENAPEN CVDDIMD
OZVN W MZKNVYZYK PLT LY VLI CNLOC
W MWES LB ELYBZTDYED.

                              —TLAK HWEMDLT

• • • • • • • • • • • • • • • • •

536   DZMLN ML IXZ TOPR MW EMAZ
DZMLN ML IXZ DGR WFGHIW, ZKFZYI
IXTI IXZ DGR WFGHIW XTJZ TCHEI
WHYZOJMWMGL.   —DETAZ FETOA

• • • • • • • • • • • • • • • • •

537   T DBZNV ACUCL LCPV P GBBF TO TW
DCLC IBJJTGNC OBL RC WB WPNF EPNO
PA EBZL DTWE WEC RPA DEB DLBWC TW.

                              —DBBVLBD DTNJBA

538   LC'Q SMTH JGT CSW RGHWTZ
VWZWTMCLGZ CG IZHWTQCMZH
CSGTWMI, XSG ELAWH DWQLHW M KGZH
DIC HLHZ'C GXZ XMCWT QOLQ GT M
QZGTOWE.   —DLEE AMIVSMZ

• • • • • • • • • • • • • • • • •

539   CKEHQNF QN R ZAKKI HRKEAREC.
JFRJ CDMHRQKN UFI UC MROW GAO XRO
GK JFC LOQYCURI RKL LOQYC GAO XRO
GK JFC MROWURI.   —TROW EORNNG

• • • • • • • • • • • • • • • • •

540   AQXGRO OEZXR IR. G UJL'F VZLF FJ
SQF IT PZGFD GL SRJSWR VDJ VRXRL'F
OIZXF RLJQBD FJ BRF JQF JP AQXT UQFT.
                —IJLGEZ SGSRX

541   WKRVR FZ SN UNFSW HW MKFEK

ONY EHS ZHO, "MRQQ, F'G ZYEERZZLYQ

SNM. F GFAKW HZ MRQQ WHJR H SHU."

—EHVVFR LFZKRV

• • • • • • • • • • • • • • • • •

542   CJU SUIODB CJUSU ISU OD QUN

QUPIMU RDMGCGHGIBO GO CJIC GC GO

CDD PVHJ CSDVLMU CD RVC PIXU-VR DB

CND QIHUO.   —PIVSUUB PVSRJT

• • • • • • • • • • • • • • • • •

543   S XSBPQPXB PX S VSL GJU

RPXTUYNQX HLEWNSXSLB BJPLCX SFUHB

JPVXNWK SLR BJNL XSDX BJNV SFUHB

UBJNQ ENUEWN.   —ENBNQ VTSQBJHQ

544   EGEDWU-EGED XDZFDEW HA WLD

XDHXYD GE WLD JHZYO RZD AHHYK, REO

WLD ZDKW HA SK RZD GE NZDRW

ORENDZ HA FHEWRNGHE.

—WLHZEWHE JGYODZ

• • • • • • • • • • • • • • • • •

545   YGN CITSHYWBAN SU W TZDPCA

MTNWRNH DNWHM WB CBJNHMN

HNPWYCSBMGCT YS YGN BZIDNH SU

ICAHSTGSBNM CBYS VGCAG GN

MTNWRM.   —VCPPCWI ISHXWB

• • • • • • • • • • • • • • • • •

546   NG'A FYG GKUG N BMNGI BIEE, N

DXAG LYF'G BMNGI QULEW RIMW YZGIF,

UFL GKUG OUAAIA ZYM HYYL YF

GIEIRNANYF.   —UFLW MYYFIW

547   JEB R.I. AI JEB DPUM WDRPJNM
KEBNB TXAURNB JD ZNDCDJB MDRNIBUT
AI KALBUM WDPIALBNBL XNNDOXPJ.

—OXNNM JNRLBXR

• • • • • • • • • • • • • • • • •

548   VI MVI ZM ZDI PJQQNI KEIU ZDI
VMXUZ ZVM JYLIYZJMYU MS DRPKYJZT—
XMPKYZJW NMLI KYQ ERY CMVQIX.

—KYQXI PKRXMJU

• • • • • • • • • • • • • • • • •

549   G'W ICKRVLSXVZ KLUX SPXUX GK AR
VGDX RA WIUK. GS'K ARS VGKSXQ RA
WZ QILFPSXU'K BPRAX CGVV.

—VIUUZ WISSPXJK

550   ICK YBYCA, PCOY DA MIJ
POOLVVYR, OIC NY XIRY AP IEEYIV
DCYBDAINSY NK I OPXEYAYCA
MDJAPVDIC.   —SYY JDXPCJPC

• • • • • • • • • • • • • • • • •

551   UQ MHNIO EHMA XHFYNJAX UA YT
OGA WNYCTXI YM HTJYUSVOHRHDHOQ,
VTX RAIHXAI H OGHTZ IGA GVOAX UA.
                              —YIJVN DAFVTO

• • • • • • • • • • • • • • • • •

552   X SNISWPKU NO FSA BNEV KL
QAPOKE USK GKKBO XF X OXROXIA
XEV FSNEBO KL QNMXOOK.
                    —XGXE QXFPNMB SAPWAPF

553 NTGA XI PD QLZAXWIA GPVXAXLC?
X'OW GQNGDI NGCAWE AL ATYLN GC
WJJ XCAL GC WQWMAYXM ZGC.

—LQXOWY TWYZLYE

. . . .

554 UX AVK CMCO GCC HC WCPPULW
RCFPCL RA PYC BVTUSC, BKP IVZL PYC
MUICV SFHCOF FLI SVHC YCTB HC.

—RVRSFP WVTIPYZFUP

. . . .

555 LO'G FZMAOJ LSG PSEO WMIZAJ.
LO ZGOJ FI DO KSGOMWDPO WAJ
JOCMOGGOJ, AIR LO'G JOCMOGGOJ
WAJ KSGOMWDPO.   —JWBSJ EMIGF

556   WBQAQ KAQ FDYQ SGQKF

FD HADVN WBKW DVCL K MQAL

SVWQCCSNQVW IQAFDV EDJCG

ZQCSQMQ WBQY.

—NQDANQ DAHQCC

● ● ● ● ● ● ● ● ● ● ● ● ● ● ● ● ● ●

557   GQJO OS PQKY RSFY AVJ? RYJB

RSFYSJY Q OYDYXNQF RQCZJX, "ZXJSNY

AZNRO OYDYXNQF."   —PYJJC CSVJXFQJ

● ● ● ● ● ● ● ● ● ● ● ● ● ● ● ● ● ●

558   ECMVPEUV EPV: E TPLFRUV LQ

VAS RWVEKSWVSF MLKF CG VAS

RWTPOWUOTKSF VL VAS RVVSPKG

CSZOKFSPSF.   —EK UETT

559 Y'J ZQHRB HA ZMUYEI FMNGV. FSG
HECU FSYEI YV—Y WHRCB XG KRVF MV
ZQHRB AHQ SMCA FSG JHEGU.

—MQFSRQ IHBAQGU

• • • • • • • • • • • • • • • • •

560 JBF ITYO R JTERP JTUM HYP FYRUO
HT ABRPXY R ERP'O BRCVHO RPI HBYP
ATELWRVP HBRH BY'O PTH HBY ERP OBY
ERUUVYI?   —CRUCUR OHUYVORPI

• • • • • • • • • • • • • • • • •

561 BXMDXKORB U SRM R OPW. DPORB
U'Y R OPW. DPYPKKPS U'ZZ NKPEREZB
MDUZZ EX R OPW. MUWC! DCXKX'M MP
ZUDDZX CPNX JPK ROHRFIXYXFD.

—MFPPNB

562   SCZUDPZZ UZ DPMPO ZX LPRFJLI RZ
BLPD, FUVP R GLUGVPD, UJ TCZJ QX R
GPOJRUD RTXCDJ XK ZGORJGLUDH KXO
BLRJ UJ HPJZ.   —LPDOI KXOQ

• • • • • • • • • • • • • • • • • •

563   FZT GLQQTNTZXT VTSATTZ GTPSU
PZG SPRTD LD SUPS GTPSU GFTDZ'S HTS
AFNDT TYTNE SLIT XFZHNTDD ITTSD.
                              —NFE DXUPTQTN

• • • • • • • • • • • • • • • • • •

564   LU K RWS QLUEZWP K GTQXEZWY
GKU QKCW K QLPZKCW PT NYWKZ ZOKZ
LZ STEDM ZKCW QKUV QWU QKUV
QTUZOP ZT WBEKD LZ.
                        —QWYDW D. QWKGOKQ

565   F JGPKE XDWZMX WZDW WZM

VMGVKM JGHEMX JZA F JDCH'W

VXMCFEMHW WZDH JZA F DS.

—CDKSGH V. UZDCM

• • • • • • • • • • • • • • • • • •

566   EGNC R VRC FNDUFNZ RCL DUVN UZ

CQ WQCXNF QS TFXNCD UVIQFDRCHN,

GUZ HQWWNRXTNZ XNCNFRWWJ

IFNZNCD GUV EUDG R ERDHG.

—F.H. ZGNFFUSS

• • • • • • • • • • • • • • • • • •

567   SAPF P XVFZ ABHPG YMVGRQ EPG'F

MKEAPGRM XTDYWMHQ. MCMTZDGM

LGDSQ MKPEFWZ ADS FD QDWCM FAM

DFAMT OMWWDS'Q.   —DWVG HVWWMT

568 VL USK TSH'M PVHT WPYNNVHD

NVAY IYZHKM OKMMYQ LSQ MRS SQ

MEQYY TZUW, IYZHKM OKMMYQ VW

TZQH DSST WEZXVHD FQYZP.

—OZQQU DSNTRZMYQ

• • • • • • • • • • • • • • • • •

569 SERI R VZTNL IEOGW IERI IEK SEKKV

SRM OGXKGIKB HKPJYK IEK RZIJCJHOVK;

JIEKYSOMK, TRG LJZ OCRWOGK IEK RSPZV

MTYKKTEOGW?

—MRCZKV EJPPKGMIKOG

• • • • • • • • • • • • • • • • •

570 T'P F WUNPULSVJ. LSFL'Z F WJVFL

LSTQW LU EV, F WUNPULSVJ. ZSV BFAAZ

PV WUN MUJ ZSUJL. LSFL'Z BYLV. T

LFYWSL SVJ LSFL. —VAAVQ NVWVQVJVZ

571   MHW YIHZ ZUJI MHW'FJ MHWIN,
MHW LUVIY MHWF ARA'T TWGJFERI. LUJI
MHW NFHZ WG RIA FJRKVPJ UJ'T DWTL R
FJNWKRF NWM ZUH ZJRFT R BRGJ.

—ARSJ RLJKK

• • • • • • • • • • • • • • • • •

572   TZ TM UKII ZP FKRKRLKF ZOJZ ZOK
KWZTFK XWTYKFMK, UTZO PWK
ZFTBITWH KAEKNZTPW, TM EPRNPMKC PB
PZOKFM.   —DPOW JWCFKU OPIRKM

• • • • • • • • • • • • • • • • •

573   SF'L OPLF BL LPGI B GINSJI QDG
QBSVPGI FD ABTI FAI GSZAF SEIB QSQFW
WIBGL FDD LDDX BL QSTI WIBGL FDD
VBFI.   —O.G. JVBFF

574   EGGZSIMM VBPGARGAIZNO ZQN
ZXG XGAOZ NMNWNBZO GE IWNAVPIB
OGPVNZJ: YVGMNBPN RTBPZTIZNH SJ
PGWWVZZNN WNNZVBCO.

—CNGACN XVMM

• • • • • • • • • • • • • • • • •

575   AQTDRSPJM PC R EJMQAXBTZ
SOPMI. PB HJT DJTZQM'S CPIM HJTX
MRGA HJT'Q ORWA SJ URH DRCO.

—XPSR GRA KXJEM

• • • • • • • • • • • • • • • • •

576   VKRYX SV VYLNH WKEN DEYSIH VK
CSTT KZV VJN SIOKWN VYM CKEW VJYI
SV RKNH VK WYLN VJN SIOKWN.

—YTCENR N. INZWYI

577   ESRTWTGS: PQS FGDO NVFJSZZTFG

PQMP DMAFVZ TGWSZZMGPDO PF

RSZPVFO PQS VSMZFG JFV TPZ

SHTZPSGWS.   —IMESZ AVOWS

• • • • • • • • • • • • • • • • •

578   TLHTKL DKUDQV MHEL BT WH EL

DZJ VDQ WADW EQ VEHFNZO NV

CHWALXNZO WALE. ULKK NW'V

FNKKNZO EL!   —ULZJQ KNLCEDZ

• • • • • • • • • • • • • • • • •

579   K QRD DGF CKVV WRE ZA INEQFEA.

PRJ K OPRJ JGHD DGRIF MRTDREI JFEF

JFHEKPQ ZHIOI WRE.

              —UHZFI G. CREFP

580   CQOWUP QJ BWXQHO AHS
BMJCWHK VAA UWHP. UAHAOWUP
QJ VBS JWUS.   —SGQNW ZAHO

• • • • • • • • • • • • • • • • • •

581   YLBMRY—ZYBR CK EJOLVIG BJL
BMZBKG IJOVDOVU RQ ALEQJL RYLK
EBMM IQZV.

—WYKMMOG IOMMLJ

• • • • • • • • • • • • • • • • • •

582   MECZCRCU W QCCX XWYC
CPCUOWVC, W XWC LSMZ JZGWX
GEC QCCXWZT HNVVCV.

—USKCUG F. EJGOEWZV

583   L RWUK DYKCO W MZO ZE OLIK
DKWVJRLCB ORVZABR ORK SLSMK EZV
MZZYRZMKD.   —X.J. ELKMND

• • • • • • • • • • • • • • • • •

584   ROG QXWWGVGSNG IGRCGGS
QXPYVNG DSQ KGMDK HGFDVDRXYS XH
RODR D KGMDK HGFDVDRXYS MXPGH D
OLHIDSQ RXTG RY OXQG OXH TYSGE.

                              —AYOSSE NDVHYS

• • • • • • • • • • • • • • • • •

585   XQ IC NYKSW HCSS YKO
CDTCOXCENCH QYO IAGL LACM NYHL
KH, IC'W VC PXSSXYEGXOCH.

                              —GVXRGXS FGE VKOCE

586   JSC NYC KSYZ JYMT ASBBSK BEYC
FRJSC. 'NYPTS RCGI BES JYGS JXCZ
NRPGZ NRCNSXUS RQ RCS XCNE
SLPYGXCH Y EPCZKSZ JXGST.

—KRTSYCCS YKCRGZ

•••••••••••••••••

587   R ONFFPB RG WROS JUBNZ—AXJ
NW WUUG NW R DXGQ XH JDP HDUGP,
R CPFJ N FUJ APJJPI.

—AXGGZ DUPWJ NGB EUDG IPRGPI

•••••••••••••••••

588   XBB KJP KJHYLI H GPXBBU BHDP KA
RA XGP PHKJPG HZZAGXB, HBBPLXB, AG
NXKKPYHYL.

—XBPSXYRPG QAABBTAKK

589   KLIZJ TNZ NZMZTDZXGP TUUFBZX LQ
DTEAJY DVAJYB MZNBLJTGGP. A UTJJLD
BZZ TJP LDVZN VLJZBD KTP LQ DTEAJY
DVZI.   —ITNPT ITJJZB

• • • • • • • • • • • • • • • • • •

590   CG TNAAFB SGP SNDDZYO N PGTNC
TNO RF TNBBZFI, ZA NYPNOL DYFNLFL
SFB AG IZLMGUFB ASNA ASFBF ZL N
CZMF TNC PSG PZLSFL ASNA LSF PFBF
CGA.   —S.Y. TFCMHFC

• • • • • • • • • • • • • • • • • •

591   IT NBO ENTDGPZAO KVZO RN VFT,
"P GZFO QBFTENT DNG RYZ FGRPWBZV."
P KVZO RN VFT, "GPCYR, P CN RN
VYNQQPAC IFBBV DNG RYZ IKVPW."

                                         —GPRF GKOAZG

592   XW MPNON L HAON DQO L JOQUNS
PNLOM? QSTI MXZN HLS PNLT IQAO
JOQUNS PNLOM, RAWM LW MXZN HLS
PNLT PXW JOQUNS LOZW LSF TNBW.

—ZXWW VXBBI

• • • • • • • • • • • • • • • • •

593   ILRER JG ZW ADRXGKER JZ LXMJZN
ZWILJZN IW TW; ILR PKZ JG JZ LXMJZN
DWIG IW TW XZT ZWI TWJZN JI.

—BXES CJDGZW DJIIDR

• • • • • • • • • • • • • • • • •

594   S HWAYMLSC WO S LSZ QJM
SYQSRO BULULGUBO S QMLSZ'O
GWBCJHSR GPC ZUDUB BULULGUBO
JUB SVU.   —BMGUBC IBMOC

595   VKS BQEF CP Q VEIS WEIGK ... XG

VKQV LCI PQDD XA DCTS PXEGV QAN

OECYS PCE ESQGCAG QPVSEJQEN.

—GKQAQ QDSRQANSE

• • • • • • • • • • • • • • • • • •

596   RITTLAZU I RIZ AB GAEQ KFLAZU

BYRQDWAZU LYF'HQ KQQZ IORATAZU SYT

I GYZU DARQ AZ I BWYX PAZOYP. LYF RIL

GYHQ AD PWQZ LYF UQD AD WYRQ, KFD

AD OYQBZ'D IGPILB UY PADW

QHQTLDWAZU QGBQ.   —CQIZ EQTT

• • • • • • • • • • • • • • • • • •

597   WML HFTNLIDRV WMKYA FZDRW F

XDSL PKWM F EDRZIL HLFYKYA KV WMFW

KW OFY DYIQ HLFY DYL WMKYA.

—TDYYKL ZFTSLT

598   DPZEUN QCI: DQ OCF UCBN UEXN
MDCXF ERQ EW CUNXDZCP SNESMN
QOCP VEMW.   —KDMM XEVNXF

• • • • • • • • • • • • • • • • • •

599   Q DMFME HDML LIWU EMWZ
IWTTQDMJJ LWJ YDUQZ Q PVU
XWEEQMG. WDG SO UIMD QU LWJ UVV
ZWUM.   —XWM HWYBBXWDD

• • • • • • • • • • • • • • • • • •

600 PM LZB TIR'H XIL IRLHYPRF FZZV IQZBH
XZSDZRD, XPH JPFYH YDJD QL SD.
                    —INPTD JZZXDKDNH NZRFCZJHY

HINTS

HINTS

CRYPTOGRAM HINTS

The first letter is the code letter;
the second is the letter the code letter represents.

01	J represents G	**21**	Z represents G	**41**	Z represents C
02	H represents F	**22**	O represents N	**42**	B represents N
03	S represents G	**23**	S represents Y	**43**	X represents D
04	I represents V	**24**	H represents Y	**44**	W represents C
05	T represents V	**25**	A represents D	**45**	I represents B
06	S represents M	**26**	L represents M	**46**	I represents L
07	K represents R	**27**	E represents Y	**47**	O represents W
08	T represents N	**28**	Z represents B	**48**	X represents D
09	M represents V	**29**	A represents U	**49**	W represents E
10	W represents M	**30**	D represents B	**50**	U represents O
11	M represents N	**31**	R represents N	**51**	V represents M
12	A represents F	**32**	Z represents C	**52**	L represents U
13	K represents R	**33**	H represents O	**53**	O represents L
14	B represents M	**34**	M represents O	**54**	M represents T
15	C represents W	**35**	G represents H	**55**	R represents W
16	F represents C	**36**	D represents R	**56**	Z represents M
17	M represents W	**37**	F represents H	**57**	G represents S
18	O represents C	**38**	R represents S	**58**	O represents S
19	E represents M	**39**	J represents T	**59**	I represents U
20	V represents E	**40**	C represents T	**60**	X represents D

61	I represents D	**88**	Y represents B	**115**	W represents B
62	T represents V	**89**	R represents P	**116**	G represents L
63	O represents W	**90**	Q represents B	**117**	F represents N
64	L represents T	**91**	J represents U	**118**	R represents S
65	D represents Y	**92**	A represents I	**119**	X represents N
66	G represents B	**93**	K represents Y	**120**	V represents Y
67	S represents Y	**94**	T represents H	**121**	G represents Y
68	E represents T	**95**	O represents G	**122**	X represents I
69	P represents N	**96**	Z represents W	**123**	W represents G
70	D represents I	**97**	Y represents N	**124**	S represents N
71	S represents H	**98**	J represents N	**125**	K represents W
72	M represents H	**99**	Y represents T	**126**	Y represents S
73	C represents N	**100**	W represents B	**127**	M represents T
74	J represents R	**101**	D represents T	**128**	E represents F
75	N represents O	**102**	Q represents I	**129**	N represents W
76	D represents P	**103**	U represents N	**130**	F represents N
77	H represents R	**104**	I represents B	**131**	V represents S
78	Y represents F	**105**	A represents V	**132**	B represents Y
79	V represents C	**106**	D represents Y	**133**	G represents N
80	T represents P	**107**	V represents W	**134**	S represents W
81	B represents I	**108**	G represents L	**135**	B represents C
82	A represents P	**109**	T represents R	**136**	F represents H
83	V represents N	**110**	E represents N	**137**	N represents O
84	I represents N	**111**	H represents D	**138**	D represents B
85	M represents Y	**112**	T represents W	**139**	B represents R
86	K represents I	**113**	O represents P	**140**	R represents N
87	Z represents F	**114**	D represents S	**141**	W represents A

142 F represents G
143 Y represents K
144 V represents W
145 L represents G
146 B represents R
147 Z represents L
148 M represents S
149 B represents D
150 G represents S
151 Q represents I
152 T represents G
153 C represents N
154 F represents G
155 J represents R
156 X represents L
157 Z represents O
158 Q represents N
159 X represents G
160 O represents A
161 M represents B
162 F represents S
163 U represents O
164 G represents I
165 H represents E
166 P represents M
167 L represents R
168 E represents Y

169 P represents S
170 S represents C
171 A represents S
172 T represents U
173 F represents N
174 D represents Y
175 I represents H
176 B represents D
177 Z represents W
178 I represents N
179 E represents K
180 B represents T
181 D represents P
182 J represents V
183 G represents Y
184 R represents S
185 B represents E
186 Y represents G
187 X represents U
188 D represents W
189 W represents N
190 V represents G
191 X represents G
192 U represents T
193 L represents I
194 I represents F
195 Y represents F

196 I represents N
197 I represents E
198 I represents U
199 N represents Y
200 O represents T
201 J represents D
202 I represents L
203 H represents B
204 A represents H
205 X represents E
206 K represents U
207 M represents H
208 P represents S
209 Y represents H
210 I represents E
211 O represents W
212 K represents V
213 V represents F
214 T represents G
215 C represents F
216 N represents S
217 G represents S
218 E represents H
219 E represents L
220 M represents N
221 J represents E
222 S represents H

223 Z represents P
224 V represents L
225 T represents M
226 O represents D
227 K represents W
228 G represents U
229 P represents F
230 C represents H
231 X represents B
232 G represents I
233 U represents W
234 H represents C
235 H represents A
236 P represents R
237 E represents N
238 M represents O
239 P represents N
240 D represents E
241 J represents D
242 F represents I
243 Q represents C
244 I represents E
245 Z represents D
246 A represents R
247 M represents P
248 R represents N
249 M represents H

250 F represents W
251 E represents L
252 F represents O
253 Z represents R
254 A represents T
255 M represents P
256 V represents Y
257 F represents A
258 N represents I
259 Z represents U
260 Y represents A
261 V represents C
262 M represents V
263 I represents A
264 R represents C
265 T represents U
266 J represents N
267 S represents C
268 B represents M
269 P represents Y
270 S represents R
271 S represents E
272 W represents O
273 B represents W
274 G represents N
275 X represents H
276 X represents B

277 Q represents M
278 W represents G
279 R represents F
280 R represents V
281 U represents L
282 T represents C
283 D represents P
284 V represents I
285 K represents M
286 E represents W
287 X represents T
288 R represents B
289 X represents U
290 X represents W
291 O represents G
292 Z represents K
293 Z represents T
294 V represents G
295 T represents F
296 N represents B
297 G represents Y
298 F represents W
299 G represents O
300 X represents G
301 K represents V
302 L represents M
303 B represents O

304 G represents L

305 Y represents C

306 W represents P

307 K represents R

308 V represents E

309 C represents G

310 K represents R

311 S represents H

312 P represents I

313 D represents S

314 L represents E

315 A represents T

316 J represents M

317 G represents A

318 X represents H

319 W represents D

320 X represents M

321 D represents B

322 P represents V

323 P represents L

324 J represents P

325 X represents K

326 Y represents M

327 T represents E

328 X represents J

329 W represents N

330 L represents I

331 G represents A

332 N represents C

333 F represents A

334 D represents W

335 O represents G

336 X represents D

337 E represents L

338 D represents M

339 C represents E

340 I represents P

341 W represents C

342 G represents O

343 V represents D

344 H represents M

345 Y represents R

346 U represents W

347 T represents S

348 K represents O

349 N represents Y

350 F represents Y

351 S represents N

352 S represents K

353 K represents L

354 N represents I

355 P represents W

356 L represents R

357 W represents N

358 D represents C

359 B represents H

360 B represents V

361 T represents N

362 V represents U

363 R represents D

364 H represents B

365 J represents K

366 U represents W

367 B represents A

368 P represents O

369 V represents D

370 U represents R

371 S represents W

372 H represents N

373 R represents V

374 T represents R

375 J represents O

376 P represents I

377 C represents H

378 U represents N

379 L represents M

380 Z represents E

381 P represents O

382 Y represents D

383 T represents D

384 A represents E

385 A represents S
386 Q represents K
387 L represents I
388 M represents L
389 T represents S
390 L represents M
391 D represents A
392 K represents D
393 R represents F
394 F represents W
395 Q represents D
396 R represents N
397 I represents D
398 O represents A
399 F represents P
400 K represents T
401 Q represents L
402 A represents O
403 P represents C
404 N represents R
405 H represents O
406 S represents A
407 C represents D
408 H represents E
409 T represents G
410 I represents A
411 L represents H

412 R represents T
413 R represents C
414 J represents O
415 Y represents H
416 Q represents P
417 C represents U
418 B represents M
419 I represents E
420 B represents E
421 Y represents I
422 C represents L
423 L represents F
424 X represents Y
425 L represents E
426 R represents M
427 N represents A
428 P represents W
429 Y represents M
430 R represents O
431 X represents T
432 A represents P
433 C represents U
434 J represents P
435 Z represents O
436 Z represents C
437 S represents V
438 J represents D

439 L represents Y
440 G represents A
441 I represents W
442 Q represents L
443 G represents M
444 I represents R
445 P represents V
446 U represents O
447 R represents T
448 R represents M
449 M represents F
450 N represents C
451 Y represents E
452 S represents H
453 U represents T
454 A represents R
455 T represents U
456 E represents T
457 R represents E
458 C represents O
459 G represents N
460 G represents H
461 H represents F
462 I represents W
463 T represents F
464 Z represents N
465 L represents H

466 Z represents I

467 U represents L

468 J represents C

469 D represents G

470 N represents M

471 K represents C

472 R represents N

473 B represents A

474 T represents Y

475 M represents T

476 P represents R

477 C represents G

478 Y represents V

479 X represents P

480 G represents P

481 B represents I

482 X represents W

483 C represents G

484 J represents C

485 X represents M

486 E represents Y

487 Y represents D

488 X represents C

489 L represents E

490 F represents C

491 Z represents L

492 O represents D

493 M represents F

494 Z represents T

495 C represents D

496 N represents L

497 Y represents P

498 Y represents H

499 Z represents D

500 Y represents P

501 H represents F

502 M represents L

503 G represents S

504 H represents M

505 F represents U

506 M represents O

507 K represents I

508 N represents H

509 K represents G

510 F represents C

511 Q represents U

512 M represents R

513 V represents E

514 B represents R

515 G represents S

516 T represents U

517 T represents C

518 U represents L

519 N represents S

520 O represents L

521 M represents P

522 A represents G

523 M represents U

524 M represents W

525 J represents U

526 Z represents G

527 M represents S

528 Z represents O

529 C represents V

530 K represents C

531 V represents R

532 Y represents D

533 R represents T

534 G represents C

535 E represents C

536 X represents H

537 D represents W

538 X represents W

539 I represents Y

540 T represents Y

541 M represents W

542 Q represents F

543 V represents M

544 Y represents L

545 T represents P

546 E represents L

547 R represents U

548 P represents M

549 W represents M

550 O represents C

551 X represents D

552 B represents K

553 Q represents L

554 B represents P

555 M represents R

556 A represents R

557 J represents N

558 C represents B

559 A represents F

560 I represents D

561 C represents H

562 L represents H

563 Z represents N

564 C represents K

565 V represents P

566 E represents W

567 S represents W

568 P represents M

569 V represents L

570 W represents G

571 N represents G

572 R represents M

573 Q represents F

574 P represents C

575 Q represents D

576 W represents M

577 D represents L

578 E represents M

579 Q represents G

580 O represents G

581 Z represents W

582 K represents B

583 D represents S

584 O represents H

585 V represents B

586 N represents C

587 A represents B

588 Q represents W

589 L represents O

590 P represents W

591 I represents M

592 P represents H

593 I represents T

594 G represents B

595 G represents S

596 C represents J

597 H represents M

598 U represents M

599 L represents W

600 C represents W

ANSWERS

ANSWERS

Introduction: If at first you don't succeed, try, try again.

1   The brain is a wonderful organ; it starts the minute you get up in
     the morning and does not stop until you get to the office.
                                                              —Robert Frost

2   There are two times in a man's life when he should not speculate:
     when he can't afford it, and when he can.   —Mark Twain

3   Why is it when we talk to God, we're said to be praying, but when
     God talks to us, we're schizophrenic?   —Lily Tomlin

4   The great thing about the movies is you're giving people little tiny
     pieces of time that they never forget.   —Jimmy Stewart

5   Everywhere I go I'm asked if I think the university stifles writers.
     My opinion is that they don't stifle enough of them.
                                                         —Flannery O'Connor

6   We didn't all come over on the same ship, but we're all in the same
     boat.   —Bernard Baruch

7   It took me seventeen years to get three thousand hits in baseball. I did it in one afternoon on the golf course.   —Hank Aaron

8   There's no trick to being a humorist when you have the whole government working for you.   —Will Rogers

9   I often have long conversations with myself, and I am so clever that sometimes I don't understand a single word I am saying.
    —Oscar Wilde

10   Nearly all men can stand adversity, but if you want to test a man's character, give him power.   —Abraham Lincoln

11   Sometimes it's necessary to go a long distance out of the way in order to come back a short distance correctly.   —Edward Albee

12   We owe a lot to Thomas Edison. If it weren't for him, we'd be watching television by candlelight.   —Milton Berle

13   Never tell people how to do things. Tell them what to do and they will surprise you with their ingenuity.   —George Patton

14   Too many people expect wonders from democracy, when the most wonderful thing of all is just having it.   —Walter Winchell

15   A celebrity is someone who works hard all his life to become well-known, and then wears dark glasses to avoid being recognized.
    —Fred Allen

16   The way to catch a knuckleball is to wait until the ball stops rolling and then pick it up.   —Bob Uecker

ANSWERS

17 There are two insults no human being will endure: that he has no sense of humor, and that he has never known trouble.

—Sinclair Lewis

18 I've over-educated myself in all the things I shouldn't have known at all. —Noël Coward

19 It took me fifteen years to discover I had no talent for writing, but I couldn't give it up because by that time I was too famous.

—Robert Benchley

20 You may be disappointed if you fail, but you are doomed if you don't try. —Beverly Sills

21 The only thing I regret about my past is the length of it. If I had to live my life again, I'd make the same mistakes, only sooner.

—Tallulah Bankhead

22 I maintain that the phrase "a long poem" is simply a contradiction in terms. —Edgar Allan Poe

23 People learn something every day, and a lot of times it's that what they learned the day before was wrong. —Bill Vaughan

24 We've had trickle-down economics in the country for years now, and most of us aren't even damp yet. —Molly Ivins

25 Do not the most moving moments of our lives find us all without words? —Marcel Marceau

26 Middle age is the awkward period when Father Time starts catching up with Mother Nature. —Harold Coffin

27 Getting divorced just because you don't love a man is almost as silly as getting married just because you do.   —Zsa Zsa Gabor

28 Never lend books, for no one ever returns them; the only books I have in my library are books that other folk have lent me.
                                                                —Anatole France

29 The trouble with equality is that we only desire it with our superiors.   —Henry Becque

30 I don't think of all the misery but of all the beauty that still remains.   —Anne Frank

31 There are two things that will be believed of any man whatsoever, and one of them is that he has taken to drink. —Booth Tarkington

32 A vegetarian is somebody who won't eat anything that can have children.   —David Brenner

33 You can live a lifetime and, at the end of it, know more about other people than you know about yourself.   —Beryl Markham

34 Human beings are the only creatures on earth that allow their children to come back home.   —Bill Cosby

35 I never could understand how two men can write a book together; to me that's like three people getting together to have a baby.
                                                                —Evelyn Waugh

36 The trouble with life in the fast lane is that you get to the other end in an awful hurry.   —John Jensen

ANSWERS

37   One doesn't discover new lands without consenting to lose sight of the shore for a very long time.   —André Gide

38   A study of economics usually reveals that the best time to buy anything is last year.   —Marty Allen

39   Man's mind stretched to a new idea never goes back to its original dimensions.   —Oliver Wendell Holmes

40   If the public likes you, you're good. Shakespeare was a common, down-to-earth writer in his day.   —Mickey Spillane

41   Life is easier than you'd think; all that is necessary is to accept the impossible, do without the indispensable, and bear the intolerable.   —Kathleen Norris

42   I am only a public entertainer who has understood his time.   —Pablo Picasso

43   Blessed is the man who, having nothing to say, abstains from giving wordy evidence of the fact.   —George Eliot

44   Politics is not a bad profession. If you succeed there are many rewards; if you disgrace yourself you can always write a book.   —Ronald Reagan

45   The point of living, and of being an optimist, is to be foolish enough to believe the best is yet to come.   —Peter Ustinov

46   Character builds slowly, but it can be torn down with incredible swiftness.   —Faith Baldwin

47   Experience is not what happens to you; it is what you do with what happens to you.   —Aldous Huxley

48   The easiest way to convince my kids that they don't really need something is to get it for them.   —Joan Collins

49   All I need to make a comedy is a park, a policeman, and a pretty girl.   —Charlie Chaplin

50   A man begins cutting his wisdom teeth the first time he bites off more than he can chew.   —Herb Caen

51   Personally, I think if a woman hasn't met the right man by the time she's twenty-four, she may be lucky.   —Deborah Kerr

52   I used to work in a fire hydrant factory. You couldn't park anywhere near the place.   —Steven Wright

53   There are two ways of spreading light: to be the candle or the mirror that reflects it.   —Edith Wharton

54   A bore is someone who persists in holding his own views after we have enlightened him with ours.   —Malcolm Forbes

55   The trouble with the profit system has always been that it is highly unprofitable to most people.   —E. B. White

56   One of the oldest human needs is having someone to wonder where you are when you don't come home at night.
                                                       —Margaret Mead

ANSWERS

57 The only thing that saves us from the bureaucracy is its inefficiency. —Eugene McCarthy

58 My father used to say that it was wicked to go fishing on Sunday. But he never said anything about draw poker. —Grover Cleveland

59 You can build a throne with bayonets, but you can't sit on it for long. —Boris Yeltsin

60 Some books are to be tasted, others to be swallowed, and some few to be chewed and digested. —Francis Bacon

61 Parents of young children should realize that few people will find their children as enchanting as they do. —Barbara Walters

62 Great events make me quiet and calm; it is only trifles that irritate my nerves. —Queen Victoria

63 He who cannot forgive others destroys the bridge over which he himself must pass. —George Herbert

64 Old age is like everything else. To make a success of it, you've got to start young. —Fred Astaire

65 Babies are always more trouble than you thought—and more wonderful. —Charles Osgood

66 The ad in the paper said "Big Sale. Last Week." Why advertise? I already missed it. They're just rubbing it in. —Yakov Smirnoff

67 It goes without saying that you should never have more children than you have car windows. —Erma Bombeck

68   People who work sitting down get paid more than people who work standing up.   —Ogden Nash

69   If only one could have two lives: the first in which to make one's mistakes, and the second in which to profit by them.
                                                                —D. H. Lawrence

70   When people keep telling you that you can't do a thing, you kind of like to try it.   —Margaret Chase Smith

71   Washington appears to be filled with two kinds of politicians— those trying to get an investigation started, and those trying to get one stopped.   —Earl Wilson

72   Don't be humble. You're not that great.   —Golda Meir

73   The impersonal hand of government can never replace the helping hand of a neighbor.   —Hubert H. Humphrey

74   Trouble is a sieve through which we sift our acquaintances. Those too big to pass through are our friends.   —Arlene Francis

75   This will remain the land of the free only so long as it is the home of the brave.   —Elmer Davis

76   If you can keep your head when all about you are losing theirs, it's just possible you haven't grasped the situation.   —Jean Kerr

77   The remarkable thing about Shakespeare is that he really is very good, in spite of all the people who say he is very good.
                                                                —Robert Graves

ANSWERS

78   A man's got to take a lot of punishment to write a really funny
book.   —Ernest Hemingway

79   You can easily judge the character of a man by how he treats those
who can do nothing for him.   —James D. Miles

80   I hate television. I hate it as much as peanuts. But I can't stop
eating peanuts.   —Orson Welles

81   The best and most beautiful things in the world cannot be seen or
even touched. They must be felt with the heart.   —Helen Keller

82   Why is propaganda so much more successful when it stirs up
hatred than when it tries to stir up friendly feeling?
—Bertrand Russell

83   The aim of flattery is to soothe and encourage us by assuring us of
the truth of an opinion we have already formed about ourselves.
—Edith Sitwell

84   Nothing you write, if you hope to be any good, will ever come out
as you first hoped.   —Lillian Hellman

85   I have found that the best way to give advice to your children is to
find out what they want, and then advise them to do it.
—Harry Truman

86   Music must repeat the thoughts and inspirations of the people
and the times.   —George Gershwin

87   Twenty-four hour room service generally refers to the length of
time that it takes for the club sandwich to arrive. —Fran Lebowitz

ANSWERS

88 Kind words can be short and easy to speak, but their echoes are truly endless.   —Mother Teresa

89 There is no human problem which could not be solved if people would simply do as I advise.   —Gore Vidal

90 If you keep on saying things are going to be bad, you have a good chance of being a prophet.   —Isaac Bashevis Singer

91 Americans communicate through buttons, T-shirts, and bumper stickers the way some cultures use drums.   —Tim McCarthy

92 The bird of paradise alights only upon the hand that does not grasp.   —John Berry

93 Dreams say what they mean, but they don't say it in daytime language.   —Gail Godwin

94 A little rebellion now and then is a good thing, and as necessary in the political world as storms in the physical.   —Thomas Jefferson

95 I don't believe in an afterlife, although I am bringing a change of underwear.   —Woody Allen

96 If a window of opportunity appears, don't pull down the shade.
                                                        —Tom Peters

97 Every generation laughs at the old fashions, but religiously follows the new.   —Henry David Thoreau

98 There is no denying the fact that writers should be read but not seen. Rarely are they a winsome sight.   —Edna Ferber

99   A mother is not a person to lean on but a person to make leaning unnecessary.   —Dorothy Canfield Fisher

100   If a dog jumps onto your lap, it is because he is fond of you; but if a cat does the same thing, it is because your lap is warmer.
     —A. N. Whitehead

101   You can lie to your wife or your boss, but you cannot lie to your typewriter. Sooner or later you must reveal your true self in your pages.   —Leon Uris

102   Failure is the condiment that gives success its flavor.
     —Truman Capote

103   The most beautiful things in the world are the most useless: peacocks and lilies, for instance.   —John Ruskin

104   It takes a long time to heal a broken heart. But playing one of my albums can help.   —Frank Sinatra

105   All civilization has from time to time become a thin crust over a volcano of revolution.   —Havelock Ellis

106   The world is before you, and you need not take it or leave it as it was when you came in.   —James Baldwin

107   When one says that a writer is fashionable one practically always means that he is admired by people under thirty. —George Orwell

108   Autumn is a season followed immediately by looking forward to spring.   —Doug Larson

109 The rich have a passion for bargains as lively as it is pointless.
—Françoise Sagan

110 All pro athletes are bilingual. They speak English and profanity.
—Gordie Howe

111 Nothing is more difficult, and therefore more precious, than to be able to decide.   —Napoleon

112 It is a damned poor mind indeed that can't think of at least two ways of spelling any word.   —Andrew Jackson

113 Absences are a good influence in love and help keep it bright and delicate.   —Robert Louis Stevenson

114 Laughter is the shortest distance between two people.
—Victor Borge

115 A bad review is like baking a cake with all the best ingredients and having someone sit on it.   —Danielle Steel

116 The best liar is he who makes the smallest amount of lying go the longest way.   —Samuel Butler

117 A child becomes an adult when he realizes that he has a right not only to be right but also to be wrong.   —Thomas Szasz

118 Character consists of what you do on the third and fourth tries.
—James Michener

119 Unless you choose to do great things with it, it makes no difference how much power you have.   —Oprah Winfrey

ANSWERS

120 It's not a good idea to try to put your wife into a novel ... not your latest wife anyway.   —Norman Mailer

121 The number one fact about the news media is that they love fights. When you give them confrontations you get attention.
                                                —Newt Gingrich

122 Justice is a machine that, when someone has once given it the starting push, rolls on of itself.   —John Galsworthy

123 The greatest good you can do for another is not just to share your riches but to reveal to him his own.   —Benjamin Disraeli

124. When you aim for perfection, you discover it's a moving target.
                                                —George Fisher

125 Happiness is like a butterfly which appears and delights us for one brief moment, but soon flits away.   —Anna Pavlova

126 Music can measure how broad our horizons are. My mind wants to see to infinity.   —Stevie Wonder

127 If my books had been any worse I would not have been invited to Hollywood, and if they had been any better I would not have come.   —Raymond Chandler

128 Flattery is all right—if you don't inhale.   —Adlai Stevenson

129 Whatever women do they must do twice as well as men to be thought half as good. Luckily, this is not difficult.
                                                —Charlotte Whitton

130 How inappropriate to call this planet Earth when clearly it is Ocean.   —Arthur C. Clarke

131 The only thing that stops God from sending another flood is that the first one was useless.   —Nicholas Chamfort

132 You can discover more about a person in an hour of play than in a year of conversation.   —Plato

133 Life's but a walking shadow, a poor player that struts and frets his hour upon the stage, and then is heard no more.
—William Shakespeare

134 Guilt is the price we pay willingly for doing what we are going to do anyway.   —Isabelle Holland

135 I aimed at the public's heart, and by accident I hit it in the stomach.
—Upton Sinclair

136 The advance for a book should be at least as much as the cost of the lunch at which it was discussed.   —Calvin Trillin

137 If I made "Cinderella," the audience would be looking out for a body in the coach.   —Alfred Hitchcock

138 Censorship, like charity, should begin at home; but, unlike charity, it should end there.   —Clare Boothe Luce

139 Liberty, when it begins to take root, is a plant of rapid growth.
—George Washington

ANSWERS

140 If you want work well done, select a busy man; the other kind has no time. —Elbert Hubbard

141 Never insult an alligator until after you have crossed the river. —Cordell Hull

142 About the most originality that any writer can hope to achieve honestly is to steal with good judgment. —Josh Billings

143 What an author likes to write most is his signature on the back of a check. —Brendan Francis

144 A rumor without a leg to stand on will get around some other way. —John Tudor

145 Being given good material is like being assigned to bake a cake and having the batter made for you. —Rosalind Russell

146 Don't condescend to unskilled labor. Try it for half a day first. —Brooks Atkinson

147 In the music industry a legend is usually no more than someone with two consecutive hit singles. —Garry Trudeau

148 Dogs come when they're called; cats take a message and get back to you. —Mary Bly

149 Education is a progressive discovery of our own ignorance. —Will Durant

150 My wife said for our anniversary she wanted to go someplace she'd never been before. I said, "How 'bout the kitchen?"

—Rodney Dangerfield

151 Liberty means responsibility. That is why most men dread it.

—George Bernard Shaw

152 The reason grandparents and grandchildren get along so well is that they have a common enemy.   —Sam Levenson

153. Having the critics praise you is like having the hangman say you've got a pretty neck.   —Eli Wallach

154 I would venture to guess that Anon, who wrote so many poems without signing them, was often a woman.   —Virginia Woolf

155 Whatever a man prays for, he prays for a miracle. Every prayer reduces itself to this: "Great God, grant that twice two be not four."   —Ivan Turgenev

156 When it comes to foreign food, the less authentic the better.

—Gerald Nachman

157 Moderation in temper is always a virtue, but moderation in principle is always a vice.   —Thomas Paine

158 What troubles me is not that movie stars run for office, but that they find it easy to get elected.   —Shana Alexander

159 It is the malady of our age that the young are so busy teaching us that they have no time left to learn.   —Eric Hoffer

160 The winds and waves are always on the side of the ablest navigators. —Edward Gibbon

161 A book ought to be an ice pick to break up the frozen sea within us. —Franz Kafka

162 Mistakes are the usual bridge between experience and wisdom. —Phyllis Theroux

163 Happiness is beneficial for the body, but it is grief that develops the powers of the mind. —Marcel Proust

164 Good communication is as stimulating as black coffee, and just as hard to sleep after. —Anne Morrow Lindbergh

165 Satire is a sort of glass, wherein beholders do generally discover everybody's face but their own. —Jonathan Swift

166 There is so much buildup in my oven there is only room to bake a single cupcake. —Phyllis Diller

167 Whoever thinks marriage is a fifty-fifty proposition doesn't know the half of it. —Franklin P. Jones

168 If you want to make beautiful music, you must play the black and the white notes together. —Richard Nixon

169 A rose by any other name would smell as sweet, but would not cost half as much during the winter months. —George Ade

170 I have a car that I call Flattery because it gets me nowhere. —Henny Youngman

171   God gave us our memories so that we might have roses in
December.   —James M. Barrie

172   The test for whether or not you can hold a job should not be the
arrangement of your chromosomes.   —Bella Abzug

173   Man and woman are two locked caskets, of which each contains
the key to the other.   —Isak Dinesen

174   Propaganda is the art of persuading others of what you don't
believe yourself.   —Abba Eban

175   Opportunities are often things you haven't noticed the first time
around.   —Catherine Deneuve

176   If you want to kill any idea in the world today, get a committee
working on it.   —Charles F. Kettering

177   Life was a lot simpler when what we honored was father and
mother rather than all major credit cards.   —Robert Orben

178   Gossip is something that no one claims to like—but everybody
enjoys.   —Joseph Conrad

179   Man's task is to make of himself a work of art.   —Henry Miller

180   Fruitcake is the only food durable enough to become a family
heirloom.   —Russell Baker

181   Sleep, riches, and health must be interrupted to be truly enjoyed.
                                                —Jean Paul Richter

ANSWERS

ANSWERS

182　Know yourself. Don't accept your dog's admiration as conclusive evidence that you are wonderful.　　—Ann Landers

183　Sentimentality is only sentiment that rubs you the wrong way.　　—W. Somerset Maugham

184　Journalism largely consists in saying "Lord Jones is dead" to people who never knew Lord Jones was alive.　—G. K. Chesterton

185　My father was ruined in the crash. A stockbroker jumped out of a window and fell on his pushcart.　　—Jackie Mason

186　Age is a high price to pay for maturity.　　—Tom Stoppard

187　I am very fond of truth, but not at all of martyrdom.　　—Voltaire

188　If we cannot put an end to our differences, at least we can help make the world safe for diversity.　　—John F. Kennedy

189　Once, during Prohibition, I was forced to live for days on nothing but food and water.　　—W. C. Fields

190　When women go wrong, men go right after them.　　—Mae West

191　Courage is being scared to death—and saddling up anyway.　　—John Wayne

192　I have already given two cousins to the war and I stand ready to sacrifice my wife's brother.　　—Artemus Ward

193　You have all the characteristics of a popular politician: a horrible voice, bad breeding, and a vulgar manner.　　—Aristophanes

194 Be bold in what you stand for and careful what you fall for.
—Ruth Boorstin

195 To hurry through the rise and fall of a fine, full sentence is like defying the role of time in human life.   —Kenneth Clark

196 The trouble with jogging is that, by the time you realize you're not in shape for it, it's too far to walk back.   —Franklin P. Jones

197 Today's greatest labor-saving device is tomorrow.   —Tom Wilson

198 The successful revolutionary is a statesman, the unsuccessful one a criminal.   —Erich Fromm

199 Writing is easy. All you do is stare at a blank sheet of paper until drops of blood form on your forehead.   —Gene Fowler

200 While forbidden fruit is said to taste sweeter, it usually spoils faster.   —Abigail Van Buren

201 God grants liberty only to those who love it, and are always ready to guard and defend it.   —Daniel Webster

202 Love, like restaurant hash or chicken salad, must be taken with blind faith or it loses its flavor.   —Helen Rowland

203 An invasion of armies can be resisted, but not an idea whose time has come.   —Victor Hugo

204 The more he talked of his honor the faster we counted our spoons.
—Ralph Waldo Emerson

205 Lead me not into temptation; I can find the way myself.
—Rita Mae Brown

206 When nobody around you seems to measure up, it's time to check your yardstick.   —Bill Lemley

207 Any party which takes credit for the rain must not be surprised if its opponents blame it for the drought.   —Dwight W. Morrow

208 It's amazing that the amount of news that happens in the world every day always just exactly fits the newspaper.   —Jerry Seinfeld

209 A compulsion is a highbrow term for a temptation we're not trying too hard to resist.   —Hugh Allen

210 In the future everyone will be world-famous for fifteen minutes.
—Andy Warhol

211 Those who write clearly have readers; those who write obscurely have commentators.   —Albert Camus

212 Conscience is a mother-in-law whose visit never ends.
—H. L. Mencken

213 The first half of our lives is ruined by our parents and the second half by our children.   —Clarence Darrow

214 Today our problem is not making miracles, but managing them.
—Lyndon Johnson

215 One man practicing sportsmanship is far better than fifty preaching it.   —Knute Rockne

216   Things should be made as simple as possible, but not any simpler.
—Albert Einstein

217   What this country needs is more unemployed politicians.
—Edward Langley

218   Wit has truth in it; wisecracking is simply calisthenics with words.
—Dorothy Parker

219   There should be some schools called deformatories to which people are sent if they are too good to be practical.   —Samuel Butler

220   Children have more need of models than of critics.
—Carolyn Coats

221   Somewhere, something incredible is waiting to be known.
—Carl Sagan

222   Quotations, when engraved upon the memory, give you good thoughts.   —Winston Churchill

223   I have the perfect simplified tax form for the government. Why don't they just print our money with a return address on it?
—Bob Hope

224   The scientific theory I like best is that the rings of Saturn are composed entirely of lost airline luggage.   —Mark Russell

225   Immature poets imitate; mature poets steal.   —T. S. Eliot

226   Patience is something you admire in the driver behind you, and scorn in the one ahead.   —Mac McCleary

ANSWERS

227   Your assumptions are your windows on the world. Scrub them off every once in a while, or the light won't come in.   —Alan Alda

228   They say such nice things about people at their funerals that it makes me sad that I'm going to miss mine by just a few days.
—Garrison Keillor

229   The force is within you. Force yourself.   —Harrison Ford

230   Don't knock the weather; nine-tenths of the people couldn't start a conversation if it didn't change once in a while.   —Kin Hubbard

231   Anytime four New Yorkers get into a cab together without arguing, a bank robbery has just taken place.   —Johnny Carson

232   An economist is an expert who will know tomorrow why the things he predicted yesterday didn't happen.   —Earl Wilson

233   After being on the road so much I want to spend more time with my family, who I hear are wonderful people.   —Howie Mandel

234   How can you be expected to govern a country that has two hundred and forty-six kinds of cheese?   —Charles de Gaulle

235   Life is like a B-movie. You don't want to leave in the middle of it, but you don't want to see it again.   —Ted Turner

236   We were so poor we had no hot water. But it didn't matter because we had no bathtub to put it in anyway.   —Tom Dreesen

237   The average pencil is seven inches long, with just a half-inch eraser—in case you thought optimism was dead.   —Robert Brault

238 Bill Clinton's foreign policy experience stems mainly from having breakfast at the International House of Pancakes.   —Pat Buchanan

239 Instant gratification takes too long.   —Carrie Fisher

240 My job is to talk to you, and your job is to listen. If you finish first, please let me know.   —Harry Hershfield

241 One of my chief regrets during my years in the theater is that I couldn't sit in the audience and watch me.   —John Barrymore

242 I went to a restaurant that serves breakfast at any time. So I ordered French toast during the Renaissance.   —Steven Wright

243 This will never be a civilized country until we spend more money for books than we do for chewing gum.   —Elbert Hubbard

244 Thanks to the Interstate Highway System, it is now possible to travel from coast to coast without seeing anything.
                                                           —Charles Kuralt

245 Did you ever walk in a room and forget why you walked in? I think that's how dogs spend their lives.   —Sue Murphy

246 Ideas are like rabbits. You get a couple and learn how to handle them, and pretty soon you have a dozen.   —John Steinbeck

247 I haven't reported my missing credit card to the police because whoever stole it is spending less than my wife.   —Ilie Nastase

248 The best way to keep children home is to make the home atmosphere pleasant—and let the air out of the tires.   —Dorothy Parker

249　Why should people go out and pay to see bad movies when they can stay at home and see bad television for nothing?
　　　　　　　　　　　　　　　　　　　　—Samuel Goldwyn

250　Asking a working writer what he thinks about critics is like asking a lamppost how it feels about dogs.　　—Christopher Hampton

251　I'd like to see the government get out of war altogether and leave the whole field to private industry.　　　　　—Joseph Heller

252　Disney, of course, has the best casting. If he doesn't like an actor he simply tears him up.　　　　　　　—Alfred Hitchcock

253　I asked each senator about his preferences for the presidency, and ninety-six senators each received one vote.　　—John F. Kennedy

254　Middle age: when you're home on Saturday night, the telephone rings, and you hope it's the wrong number.　　—Ring Lardner

255　I think men who have a pierced ear are better prepared for marriage. They've experienced pain and bought jewelry.
　　　　　　　　　　　　　　　　　　　　—Rita Rudner

256　You're only here for a short visit. Don't hurry. Don't worry. And be sure to smell the flowers along the way.　　—Walter Hagen

257　Millions long for immortality who do not know what to do with themselves on a rainy Sunday afternoon.　　—Susan Ertz

258　If you owe your bank a hundred pounds, you have a problem; but if you owe your bank a million, it has.　　—John Maynard Keynes

259 The fastest way to succeed is to look as if you are playing by other people's rules, while quietly playing by your own.—Michael Korda

260 Lots of people think they're charitable if they give away their old clothes and things they don't want.   —Myrtle Reed

261 There's so much plastic in this culture that vinyl leopard skin is becoming an endangered synthetic.   —Lily Tomlin

262 If you live to the age of a hundred you have it made because very few people die past the age of a hundred.   —George Burns

263 Harpists spend about ninety percent of their lives tuning their harps and ten percent playing out of tune.   —Igor Stravinsky

264 Instead of giving a politician the keys to the city, it might be better to change the locks.   —Doug Larson

265 Hollywood's a place where they'll pay you a thousand dollars for a kiss, and fifty cents for your soul.   —Marilyn Monroe

266 Of the seven dwarfs, only Dopey had a shaven face. This should tell us something about the custom of shaving.   —Tom Robbins

267 I have left orders to be awakened at any time in case of national emergency, even if I'm in a cabinet meeting.   —Ronald Reagan

268 A straight line may be the shortest distance between two points, but it is by no means the most interesting.   —Doctor Who

269 I'm paranoid about everything. On my stationary bicycle I have a rearview mirror.   —Richard Lewis

270 A good listener is not someone with nothing to say. A good listener is a good talker with a sore throat.   —Katharine Whitehorn

271 Finishing second in the Olympics gets you silver. Finishing second in politics gets you oblivion.   —Richard Milhous Nixon

272 I am not willing to risk the lives of German soldiers for countries whose names we cannot spell properly.   —Volker Ruhe

273 The longest word in the English language is the one that follows the phrase, "And now a word from our sponsor."   —Hal Eaton

274 Even more exasperating than the guy who thinks he knows it all is the one who really does.   —Al Bernstein

275 I once bought my kids a set of batteries for Christmas with a note on it saying, "Toys not included."   —Bernard Manning

276 Children are the most desirable opponents at Scrabble as they are both easy to beat and fun to cheat.   —Fran Lebowitz

277 New York City now leads the world's greatest cities in the number of people around whom you shouldn't make a sudden move.
    —David Letterman

278 Why do birds sing in the morning? It's the triumphant shout: "We got through another night."   —Enid Bagnold

279 We who officially value freedom of speech above life itself seem to have nothing to talk about but the weather. —Barbara Ehrenreich

280 Ask a man which way he is going to vote, and he will probably tell you. Ask him, however, why, and vagueness is all. —Bernard Levin

281 Cleaning your house while your kids are still growing is like shoveling the walk before it stops snowing. —Phyllis Diller

282 A compromise is the art of dividing a cake in such a way that everyone believes he has the biggest piece. —Ludwig Erhard

283 I'm a philosophy major. That means I can think deep thoughts about being unemployed. —Bruce Lee

284 In Hollywood, an equitable divorce settlement means each party getting fifty percent of the publicity. —Lauren Bacall

285 Hard work and a proper frame of mind prepare you for the lucky breaks that finally come along—or don't. —Harrison Ford

286 I've gained a few pounds around the middle. The only lower-body garments I own that still fit me comfortably are towels.
—Dave Barry

287 Never brag about your ancestors coming over on the Mayflower; the immigration laws weren't as strict in those days. —Lew Lehr

288 It's strange how few of the world's great problems are solved by people who remember their algebra. —Herbert Prochnow

289 True love comes quietly, without banners or flashing lights. If you hear bells, get your ears checked. —Erich Segal

290 If you don't want to work, you have to work to earn enough money so that you won't have to work. —Ogden Nash

291 Imagination is a good horse to carry you over the ground—not a flying carpet to set you free from probability. —Robertson Davies

292 Adults are always asking little kids what they want to be when they grow up—'cause they're looking for ideas. —Paula Poundstone

293 A tourist is a fellow who drives thousands of miles so he can be photographed standing in front of his car. —Emile Ganest

294 Isn't it strange? The same people who laugh at gypsy fortune tellers take economists seriously. —Cincinnati Enquirer

295 Anyone who says businessmen deal in facts, not fiction, has never read old five-year projections. —Malcolm Forbes

296 I'm tired of all this nonsense about beauty being only skin deep. That's deep enough. What do you want, an adorable pancreas? —Jean Kerr

297 History teaches us that men and nations behave wisely once they have exhausted all other alternatives. —Abba Eban

298 They are doing away with drive-ins. Now where are the teenagers going to go to not watch a movie? —Bob Thomas

299 Only one person in a thousand is a bore, and he is interesting because he is one person in a thousand. —Harold Nicolson

300 Half of our life is spent trying to find something to do with the time we have rushed through life trying to save.   —Will Rogers

301 The advantage of having a bad memory is that, several times over, one enjoys the same good things for the first time.
—Friedrich Nietzsche

302 Okay, so God made man first, but doesn't everyone make a rough draft before they make a masterpiece?   —Courtney Huston

303 My initial response was to sue her for defamation of character, but then I realized that I had no character.   —Charles Barkley

304 Midlife crisis is that moment when you realize your children and your clothes are about the same age.   —Bill Tammeus

305 Computers will never replace the wastebasket when it comes to streamlining office work.   —Clayton Elwell

306 There is nothing more miserable in the world than to arrive in paradise and look like your passport photo.   —Erma Bombeck

307 The trouble with most of us is that we would rather be ruined by praise than saved by criticism.   —Norman Vincent Peale

308 Another flaw in the human character is that everybody wants to build and nobody wants to do maintenance.   —Kurt Vonnegut

309 The depressing thing about tennis is that no matter how good I get, I'll never be as good as a wall.   —Mitch Hedberg

310 We may not return the affection of those who like us, but we always respect their good judgment. —Libbie Fudim

311 They should put expiration dates on clothes so we would know when they go out of style. —Garry Shandling

312 I went to a high school that was so dangerous, the school newspaper had an obituary column. —Rocky Ray

313 Self-discipline is when your conscience tells you to do something and you don't talk back. —W.K. Hope

314 Irony is when you buy a suit with two pairs of pants, and then burn a hole in the coat. —Laurence Peter

315 A doctor's reputation is made by the number of eminent men who die under his care. —George Bernard Shaw

316 I figure when my husband comes home from work, if the kids are still alive, then I've done my job. —Roseanne Arnold

317 One has to look out for engineers—they begin with sewing machines and end up with the atomic bomb. —Marcel Pagnol

318 As a teenager, I was more of an anarchist, but now I want people to thrive and be harmonious. —Nicolas Cage

319 Oh dear, I never realized what a terrible lot of explaining one has to do in a murder! —Agatha Christie

320 I learned to put the toilet seat down. It makes you look like a warm, caring, sensitive human being. —Ralph Noble

ANSWERS

321 Always be nice to those younger than you, because they are the ones who will be writing about you.   —Cyril Connolly

322 A family vacation is one where you arrive with five bags, four kids and seven I-thought-you-packed-its.   —Ivern Ball

323 The first sign of maturity is the discovery that the volume knob also turns to the left.   —Chicago Tribune

324 You can't always go by expert opinion. A turkey, if you ask a turkey, should be stuffed with grasshoppers, grit, and worms.
         —Anonymous

325 Marriage is like twirling a baton, turning handsprings, or eating with chopsticks. It looks easy until you try it.   —Helen Rowland

326 When you reach for the stars, you may not quite get one, but you won't come up with a handful of mud either.   —Leo Burnett

327 A bore is a man who spends so much time talking about himself that you can't talk about yourself.   —Melville Landon

328 Will the people in the cheaper seats clap your hands? All the rest of you, if you'll just rattle your jewelry.   —John Lennon

329 I thought I'd begin by reading a poem by Shakespeare, but then I thought, why should I? He never reads any of mine.
         —Spike Mulligan

330 The older I grow, the less important the comma becomes. Let the reader catch his own breath.   —Elizabeth Clarkson Zwart

331 Sometimes the best way to convince someone he is wrong is to let him have his way. —Red O'Donnell

332 Fiction is like a spider's web, attached ever so slightly perhaps, but still attached to life at all four corners. —Virginia Woolf

333 I moved to New York City for my health. I'm paranoid and New York was the only place where my fears were justified. —Anita Weiss

334 You never see a man walking down the street with a woman who has a little potbelly and a bald spot. —Elayne Boosler

335 My neighbor asked if he could use my lawnmower and I told him of course he could, so long as he didn't take it out of my garden. —Eric Morecambe

336 Two of the hardest words in the English language to rhyme are life and love—of all words. —Stephen Sondheim

337 Whenever I hear anyone arguing for slavery, I feel a strong impulse to see it tried on him personally. —Abraham Lincoln

338 The real danger is not that computers will begin to think like men, but that men will begin to think like computers. —Sydney Harris

339 What my mother believed about cooking is that if you worked hard and prospered, someone else would do it for you. —Nora Ephron

340 Age does not depend upon years, but upon temperament and health. Some men are born old, and some never grow so.
—Tryon Edwards

341 A doctor can bury his mistakes, but an architect can only advise his client to plant vines. —Frank Lloyd Wright

342 It was going all wrong at my college interview until I nonchalantly asked, "Do you need any large donations for new buildings?"
—Todd Anderson

343 It is seldom that one parts on good terms, because if one were on good terms one would not part. —Marcel Proust

344 My doctor gave me six months to live, but when I couldn't pay the bill he gave me six months more. —Walter Matthau

345 There's one thing about children—they never go around showing snapshots of their grandparents. —Bessie & Beulah

346 Tact is the rare ability to keep silent while two friends are arguing, and you know both of them are wrong. —Hugh Allen

347 Optimism is a cheerful frame of mind that enables a teakettle to sing though in hot water up to its nose. —Harold Helfer

348 Even overweight cats instinctively know the cardinal rule: when fat, arrange yourself in slim poses. —John Weitz

349 Common sense is the most evenly distributed quantity in the world. Everyone thinks he has enough. —René Descartes

ANSWERS

350 The first time I went to an American restaurant, they asked, "How many are in your party?" I said, "Two Million." —Yakov Smirnoff

351 I have noticed that the people who are late are often so much jollier than the people who have to wait for them. —E. V. Lucas

352 Creativity is allowing oneself to make mistakes. Art is knowing which ones to keep. —Scott Adams

353 Writers have a rare power not given to anyone else; we can bore people long after we are dead. —Sinclair Lewis

354 Since I've become a central banker, I've learned to mumble with great coherence. —Alan Greenspan

355 People who have no weaknesses are terrible; there is no way of taking advantage of them. —Anatole France

356 The reason most people play golf is to wear clothes they would not be caught dead in otherwise. —Roger Simon

357 This is a free country. Folks have a right to send me letters, and I have a right not to read them. —William Faulkner

358 The key to everything is patience. You get the chicken by hatching the egg, not by smashing it. —Arnold H. Glasow

359 Speak when you are angry and you will make the best speech you will ever regret. —Ambrose Bierce

360 Life may have no meaning. Or even worse, it may have a meaning of which I disapprove. —Ashleigh Brilliant

ANSWERS

361 When people ask me if I have any spare change, I tell them I have it at home in my spare wallet.   —Nick Arnette

362 I'll give you an idea of what kind of guy he was. Saint Francis would have punched him in the mouth.   —Gene Perret

363 No man will make a great leader who wants to do it all himself or get all the credit for doing it.   —Andrew Carnegie

364 For weeks I've been telling him not to buy anything for my birthday, and he still forgot to bring me something.   —Tanya Noe

365 Use a make-up table with everything close at hand and don't rush; otherwise you'll look like a patchwork quilt.   —Lucille Ball

366 For some reason, a lot of Hollywood big shots are curious to see how they'd be drawn with bulging eyes and no chin.
   —Matt Groening

367 There are no innocent bystanders. What were they doing there in the first place?   —William S. Burroughs

368 I wish there was a knob on the TV to turn up the intelligence. There's a knob called "brightness," but it doesn't work.
   —Gallagher

369 Being a woman is a terribly difficult trade, since it consists principally of dealing with men.   —Joseph Conrad

370 A dog teaches a boy fidelity, perseverance, and to turn around three times before lying down.   —Robert Benchley

371 By working faithfully eight hours a day, you may eventually get to be a boss and work twelve hours a day. —Robert Frost

372 The reformer does not understand that people would rather be wrong and comfortable than right in jail. —Finley Peter Dunne

373 Adam invented love at first sight, one of the greatest labor-saving machines the world ever saw. —Josh Billings

374 There are more men than women in mental hospitals—which just goes to show who's driving who crazy. —Peter Veale

375 The really frightening thing about middle age is the knowledge that you'll grow out of it. —Doris Day

376 My movies are the kind they show in prisons and on airplanes because nobody can leave. —Burt Reynolds

377 Perseverance is the hard work you do after you get tired of doing the hard work you already did. —Newt Gingrich

378 You've got to be very careful if you don't know where you're going, because you might not get there. —Yogi Berra

379 An expert is a man who has made all the mistakes which can be made in a very narrow field. —Niels Bohr

380 I make a lot of money, but I don't want to talk about that. I work very hard and I'm worth every cent. —Naomi Campbell

381 My wife never lies about her age. She just tells everyone she's as old as I am. Then she lies about my age. —Robert Orben

382 The second day of a diet is always easier than the first. By the second day you're off it.   —Jackie Gleason

383 It's discouraging to think how many people are shocked by honesty, and how few by deceit.   —Noël Coward

384 An author who speaks about his own books is almost as bad as a mother who talks about her own children.   —Benjamin Disraeli

385 As I usually do when I want to get rid of someone whose conversation bores me, I pretend to agree.   —Albert Camus

386 Non-cooks think it's silly to invest two hours' work in two minutes' enjoyment; but if cooking is evanescent, so is the ballet.
                                                                —Julia Child

387 The best measure of a man's honesty isn't his income tax return. It's the zero adjust on his bathroom scale.   —Arthur C. Clarke

388 Long experience has taught me that in England nobody goes to the theater unless he or she has bronchitis.   —James Agate

389 Being president is like running a cemetery; you've got a lot of people under you and nobody's listening.   —Bill Clinton

390 They say wild animals only attack when they're cornered. I suppose that's why my goldfish was so calm when I flushed him.
                                                              —Will Gillespie

391 I should not talk so much about myself if there were anybody else whom I knew as well.   —Henry David Thoreau

ANSWERS

392 The thing with pretending you're in a good mood is that sometimes you can actually trick yourself into feeling better.
—Charles de Lint

393 I am determined my children be brought up in their father's religion, if they can find out what it is. —Charles Lamb

394 Work is the greatest thing in the world. So we should save some of it for tomorrow. —Don Herold

395 I was on a date recently, and the guy took me horseback riding. That was kind of fun, until we ran out of quarters. —Susie Loucks

396 A positive attitude will not solve all your problems, but it will annoy enough people to make it worth the effort.
—Herm Albright

397 The ultimate goal of the educational system is to shift to the individual the burden of pursuing his education. —John Gardner

398 When they call the roll in the Senate, the Senators do not know whether to answer "Present" or "Not Guilty."
—Theodore Roosevelt

399 Proposed simplified tax form: How much money did you make last year? Mail it in. —Stanton Delaplane

400 I'm all in favor of keeping dangerous weapons out of the hands of fools. Let's start with typewriters. —Solomon Short

401 A healthy male adult bore consumes each year one and a half times his own weight in other people's patience. —John Updike

402   Every man has a right to utter what he thinks truth, and every other man has a right to knock him down for it.

—Samuel Johnson

403   The future, according to some scientists, will be exactly like the past, only far more expensive.   —John Thomas Sladek

404   The reason why so few good books are written is that so few people who can write know anything.   —Walter Bagehot

405   If you want your children to improve, let them overhear the nice things you say about them to others.   —Haim Ginott

406   Never worry about the size of your Christmas tree. In the eyes of children, they are all thirty feet tall.   —Larry Wilde

407   Women and cats will do as they please, and men and dogs should relax and get used to the idea.   —Robert A. Heinlein

408   Old age is like a plane flying through a storm. Once you're aboard, there's nothing you can do about it.   —Golda Meir

409   Criticism, like rain, should be gentle enough to nourish a man's growth without destroying his roots.   —Frank A. Clark

410   Technology is a way of organizing the universe so that man doesn't have to experience it.   —Max Frisch

411   Married life teaches one invaluable lesson: to think of things far enough ahead not to say them.   —Jefferson Machamer

412   If only one could tell true love from false love as one can tell mushrooms from toadstools.   —Katharine Mansfield

413   Technological progress has merely provided us with more efficient means for going backwards.   —Aldous Huxley

414   Growing old is like being increasingly penalized for a crime you haven't committed.   —Anthony Powell

415   If life were just, we would be born old and achieve youth about the time we'd saved enough to enjoy it.   —Jim Fiebig

416   Instant availability without constant presence is probably the best role a mother can play.   —Lotte Bailyn

417   Behold the turtle: he only makes success when he sticks his neck out.   —James Bryant Conant

418   Man does not live by words alone, despite the fact that sometimes he has to eat them.   —Adlai Stevenson

419   Politicians who complain about the media are like sailors who complain about the sea.   —Enoch Powell

420   I am not a vegetarian because I love animals; I am a vegetarian because I hate plants.   —A. Whitney Brown

421   Money can't buy you happiness, but it can buy you a yacht big enough to pull up right alongside it.   —David Lee Roth

422   All marriages are happy. It's trying to live together afterwards that causes all the problems.   —Shelley Winters

423 He that has no fools, knaves, nor beggars in his family was begot by a flash of lightning.   —Thomas Fuller

424 Hollywood is a place where they place you under contract instead of under observation.   —Walter Winchell

425 I have discovered that all human evil comes from this: man's being unable to sit still in a room.   —Blaise Pascal

426 Correct me if I'm wrong, but hasn't the fine line between sanity and madness gotten finer?   —George Price

427 Do not condemn the judgment of another because it differs from your own. You may both be wrong.   —Dandemis

428 Tact is the art of making guests feel at home when that's really where you wish they were.   —George E. Bergman

429 If there's anyone listening to whom I owe money, I'm prepared to forget it if you are.   —Errol Flynn

430 The better we feel about ourselves, the fewer times we have to knock somebody else down to feel tall.   —Odetta

431 If you treat every situation as a life-and-death matter, you'll die a lot of times.   —Dean Smith

432 If moral behavior were simply following rules, we could program a computer to be moral.   —Samuel P. Ginder

433 There must be something to acupuncture—after all, you never see any sick porcupines.   —Bob Goddard

ANSWERS

434 Before most people start boasting about their family tree, they usually do a good pruning job. —O. A. Battista

435 Nobody will ever win the battle of the sexes. There's too much fraternizing with the enemy. —Henry Kissinger

436 Just when you think you've graduated from the school of experience, someone thinks up a new course. —Mary H. Waldrip

437 I have discovered the art of deceiving diplomats. I tell them the truth and they never believe me. —Camillo di Cavour

438 You may think it's a long way down the road to the drug store, but that's just peanuts to space. —Douglas Adams

439 People who make history know nothing about history. You can see that in the sort of history they make. —G. K. Chesterton

440 Before I got married, I had six theories about bringing up children; now I have six children and no theories. —John Wilmot

441 A man who views the world the same at fifty as he did at twenty has wasted thirty years of his life. —Muhammad Ali

442 In a better-ordered world, the gypsy moth would show up in October and eat the leaves after they've fallen.
—Edward Stevenson

443 Men occasionally stumble on the truth, but most of them pick themselves up and hurry off as if nothing had happened.
—Winston Churchill

444 Conversation, which is supposed to be a two-way street, is treated by many as if it were a divided highway.   —Miss Manners

445 Children have never been very good at listening to their elders, but they have never failed to imitate them.   —James Baldwin

446 Death is a very dull, dreary affair, and my advice to you is to have nothing whatever to do with it.   —W. Somerset Maugham

447 We pride ourselves on our ability to get a pizza to our door faster than an ambulance.   —Will Durst

448 I sometimes wonder if the manufacturers of foolproof items keep a fool or two on their payroll to test things.   —Alan Coren

449 My advice to you is get married: if you find a good wife you'll be happy; if not, you will become a philosopher.   —Socrates

450 If some great catastrophe is not announced every morning, we feel a certain void. Nothing in the paper today, we sigh.   —Lord Acton

451 You must get involved to have an impact. No one is impressed with the won-lost record of the referee.   —John H. Holcomb

452 It is a great help for a man to be in love with himself. For an actor, however, it is absolutely essential.   —Robert Morley

453 There are three stages of man: he believes in Santa Claus, he does not believe in Santa Claus, he is Santa Claus.   —Bob Phillips

454 The trouble with telling a good story is that it invariably reminds the other fellow of a dull one.   —Sid Caesar

ANSWERS

455 Getting an idea should be like sitting on a pin. It should make you jump up and do something. —E. L. Simpson

456 Do not worry about your problems with mathematics; I assure you mine are far greater. —Albert Einstein

457 It is often hard to distinguish between the knocks of life and those of opportunity. —Frederick Phillips

458 Opportunity is missed by most people because it is dressed in overalls and looks like work. —Thomas Edison

459 The only thing that continues to give us more for our money is the weighing machine. —George Clark

460 Love, friendship, respect do not unite people as much as a common hatred for something. —Anton Chekhov

461 The worst moment for an atheist is when he feels grateful and has no one to thank. —Wendy Ward

462 In politics, if you want anything said, ask a man; if you want anything done, ask a woman. —Margaret Thatcher

463 The closest to perfection a person ever comes is when he fills out a job application form. —Stanley J. Randall

464 My doctor told me to stop having intimate dinners for four. Unless there are three other people. —Orson Welles

465 It's a recession when your neighbor loses his job; it's a depression when you lose your own. —Harry S. Truman

466 A great many people think they are thinking when they are merely rearranging their prejudices.   —William James

467 A woman is like a tea bag—you can't tell how strong she is until you put her in hot water.   —Nancy Reagan

468 Bankruptcy stared me in the face, but one thought kept me calm; soon I'd be too poor to need an anti-theft alarm.   —Gina Rothfels

469 I loathe people who keep dogs. They are cowards who haven't got the guts to bite people themselves.   —August Strindberg

470 I find television very educating. Every time somebody turns on the set, I go into the other room and read a book.   —Groucho Marx

471 Some couples divorce because of a misunderstanding; others, because they understand each other too well.   —Evan Esar

472 There is only one difference between a madman and me. The madman thinks he is sane. I know I am mad.   —Salvador Dali

473 Congress is continually appointing fact-finding committees, when what we really need are some fact-facing committees.
                    —Roger Allen

474 Writing is the only profession where no one considers you ridiculous if you earn no money.   —Jules Renard

475 Asking an incumbent member of Congress to vote for term limits is like asking a chicken to vote for Colonel Sanders.   —Bob Inglis

476 If you think dogs can't count, try putting three dog biscuits in your pocket and then giving Fido only two of them.

—Phil Pastoret

477 I won't say ours was a tough school, but we had our own coroner. We used to write essays like "What I'm Going to Be If I Grow Up."

—Lenny Bruce

478 Dreaming permits each and every one of us to be quietly and safely insane every night of our lives.   —William Dement

479 It is great to be a blonde. With low expectations it's very easy to surprise people.   —Pamela Anderson

480 The two leading recipes for success are building a better mouse-trap and finding a bigger loophole.   —Edgar A. Schoaff

481 Middle age is having a choice between two temptations and choosing the one that'll get you home earlier.   —Dan Bennett

482 If people really liked to work, we'd still be plowing the land with sticks and transporting goods on our backs.   —William Feather

483 I don't care what you say about me, as long as you say something about me, and as long as you spell my name right.

—George M. Cohan

484 One rule of action more important than all others consists in never doing anything that someone else can do for you.

—Calvin Coolidge

485 I don't kill flies but I like to mess with their minds. I hold them above globes. They freak out and yell, "Whoa, I'm way too high!"
—Bruce Baum

486 The beauty of having a low income is that there is not enough money to buy what you don't really need.   —Ray Inman

487 Sixty minutes of thinking of any kind is bound to lead to confusion and unhappiness.   —James Thurber

488 There's nothing wrong with Southern California that a rise in the ocean level wouldn't cure.   —Ross Macdonald

489 I'm strangely proud of the wrinkles I have. What I'm giving up in elasticity, I'm gaining in wisdom.   —Suzanne Somers

490 What people do behind closed doors is certainly not my concern unless I'm behind there with 'em.   —Dolly Parton

491 Marriage is like a violin. After the beautiful music is over, the strings are still attached.   —Jacob Braude

492 He looked as if he had been poured into his clothes and had forgotten to say "when."   —P.G. Wodehouse

493 I've never been jealous. Not even when my dad finished the fifth grade a year before I did.   —Jeff Foxworthy

494 One question: if this is the information age, how come nobody knows anything?   —Robert Mankoff

495 The right to be heard does not automatically include the right to be taken seriously. —Hubert H. Humphrey

496 Three o'clock is always too late or too early for anything you want to do. —Jean-Paul Sartre

497 My wife has a slight impediment in her speech. Every now and then she stops to breathe. —Jimmy Durante

498 There's only one way to have a happy marriage, and as soon as I learn what it is I'll get married again. —Clint Eastwood

499 In science, the credit goes to the man who convinces the world, not to whom the idea first occurs. —Sir Francis Darwin

500 There exists no politician in India daring enough to attempt to explain to the masses that cows can be eaten. —Indira Gandhi

501 A friendship between reporter and source lasts only until it is profitable for one to betray the other. —Maureen Dowd

502 Politicians are people who, when they see light at the end of the tunnel, go out and buy some more tunnel. —John Quinton

503 Politicians are the same all over. They promise to build a bridge even where there is no river. —Nikita Khrushchev

504 It is not worth an intelligent man's time to be in the majority. By definition, there are already enough people to do that. —G. H. Hardy

505 Justice is the insurance we have on our lives, and obedience is the premium we pay for it.   —William Penn

506 It is a dangerous thing for a national candidate to say things that people might remember.   —Eugene McCarthy

507 As one cat said to another: Birthdays are like fur balls—the more you have, the more you gag.   —Marla Morgan

508 I believe Ronald Reagan can make this country what it once was ... a large arctic region covered with ice.   —Steve Martin

509 The great thing about democracy is that it gives every voter a chance to do something stupid.   —Art Spander

510 Going through life with a conscience is like driving your car with the brakes on.   —Budd Schulberg

511 Autobiography is an unrivaled vehicle for telling the truth about other people.   —Philip Guedalla

512 You know you are growing old when almost everything hurts, and what does not hurt does not work.   —Hy Gardner

513 Give your brain as much attention as you do your hair, and you'll be a thousand times better off.   —Malcolm X

514 If killing was the answer, we'd have solved all our problems a long time ago.   —Dick Gregory

515 Society is like a stew. If you don't keep it stirred up, you get a lot of scum on top.   —Edward Abbey

516 Nouvelle cuisine, roughly translated, means: I can't believe I paid ninety-six dollars and I'm still hungry. —Mike Kalin

517 There are only two classes of pedestrians in these days of reckless motor traffic—the quick and the dead. —Thomas Robert Dewar

518 He had occasional flashes of silence that made his conversation perfectly delightful. —Sydney Smith

519 I can't speak for any other marriage, but the secret of our marriage is that we have absolutely nothing in common.
  —Mamie Eisenhower

520 One of the lessons of history is that nothing is often a good thing to do and always a clever thing to say. —Will Durant

521 A man occupied with public or other important business cannot, and need not, attend to spelling. —Napoleon Bonaparte

522 My grandfather's a little forgetful, but he likes to give me advice. One day, he took me aside and left me there. —Ron Richards

523 The purpose of a liberal education is to make you philosophical enough to accept the fact that you will never make much money.
  —Norman Douglas

524 If it's a bill, the post office will get it to you in twenty-four hours. If it's a check, allow them a couple weeks. —Richard Needham

525 A statistician is someone who is good at figures but who doesn't have the personality to be an accountant. —Roy Hyde

526 Home is a place you grow up wanting to leave, and grow old wanting to get back to.   —John Ed Pierce

527 In order to make an apple pie from scratch, you must first create the universe.   —Carl Sagan

528 The sports page records people's accomplishments, the front page nothing but their failures.   —Justice Earl Warren

529 Some couples go over their budgets very carefully every month; others just go over them.   —Sally Poplin

530 Buying stock is exactly the same thing as going to a casino, only with no cocktail service.   —Ted Allen

531 The only person who listens to both sides of an argument is the fellow in the next apartment.   —Ruth Brown

532 Nothing is so embarrassing as watching someone do something that you said couldn't be done.   —Sam Ewing

533 Statistics are like a bikini. What they reveal is suggestive, but what they conceal is vital.   —Aaron Levenstein

534 He pasted picture postcards around goldfish bowls to make the goldfish think they were going places.   —Fred Allen

535 I still say a church steeple with a lightning rod on top shows a lack of confidence.   —Doug MacLeod

536 Being in the Army is like being in the Boy Scouts, except that the Boy Scouts have adult supervision.   —Blake Clark

537 I would never read a book if it were possible for me to talk half an hour with the man who wrote it. —Woodrow Wilson

538 It's hard for the modern generation to understand Thoreau, who lived beside a pond but didn't own water skis or a snorkel.
—Bill Vaughan

539 English is a funny language. That explains why we park our car on the driveway and drive our car on the parkway. —Mark Grasso

540 Juries scare me. I don't want to put my faith in people who weren't smart enough to get out of jury duty. —Monica Piper

541 There is no point at which you can say, "Well, I'm successful now. I might as well take a nap." —Carrie Fisher

542 The reason there are so few female politicians is that it is too much trouble to put make-up on two faces. —Maureen Murphy

543 A satirist is a man who discovers unpleasant things about himself and then says them about other people. —Peter McArthur

544 Ninety-nine percent of the people in the world are fools, and the rest of us are in great danger of contagion. —Thornton Wilder

545 The importance of a public speaker bears an inverse relationship to the number of microphones into which he speaks.
—William Morgan

546 It's not that I write well, I just don't write badly very often, and that passes for good on television. —Andy Rooney

547 The U.S. is the only country where failure to promote yourself is widely considered arrogant.   —Garry Trudeau

548 We owe to the Middle Ages the worst two inventions of humanity —romantic love and gun powder.   —Andre Maurois

549 I'm absolutely sure there is no life on Mars. It's not listed on my daughter's phone bill.   —Larry Matthews

550 Any event, once it has occurred, can be made to appear inevitable by a competent historian.   —Lee Simonson

551 My first wife divorced me on the grounds of incompatibility, and besides I think she hated me.   —Oscar Levant

552 A highbrow is the kind of person who looks at a sausage and thinks of Picasso.   —Alan Patrick Herbert

553 What is my loftiest ambition? I've always wanted to throw an egg into an electric fan.   —Oliver Herford

554 If you ever see me getting beaten by the police, put down the video camera and come help me.   —Bobcat Goldthwait

555 He's turned his life around. He used to be miserable and depressed, now he's depressed and miserable.   —David Frost

556 There are some ideas so wrong that only a very intelligent person could believe them.   —George Orwell

557 Want to have some fun? Send someone a telegram saying, "Ignore first telegram."   —Henny Youngman

558   Abstract art: a product of the untalented sold by the unprincipled to the utterly bewildered.   —Al Capp

559   I'm proud of paying taxes. The only thing is—I could be just as proud for half the money.   —Arthur Godfrey

560   Why does a woman work ten years to change a man's habits and then complain that he's not the man she married?
                          —Barbra Streisand

561   Yesterday I was a dog. Today I'm a dog. Tomorrow I'll probably still be a dog. Sigh! There's so little hope for advancement.
                          —Snoopy

562   Business is never so healthy as when, like a chicken, it must do a certain amount of scratching for what it gets.   —Henry Ford

563   One difference between death and taxes is that death doesn't get worse every time Congress meets.   —Roy Schaefer

564   In a few minutes a computer can make a mistake so great that it would take many men many months to equal it.
                          —Merle L. Meacham

565   I would rather that the people wonder why I wasn't President than why I am.   —Salmon P. Chase

566   When a man retires and time is no longer of urgent importance, his colleagues generally present him with a watch. —R. C. Sherriff

567   What a pity human beings can't exchange problems. Everyone knows exactly how to solve the other fellow's.   —Olin Miller

568   If you don't mind smelling like peanut butter for two or three days, peanut butter is darn good shaving cream.
—Barry Goldwater

569   What a lucky thing that the wheel was invented before the automobile; otherwise, can you imagine the awful screeching?
—Samuel Hoffenstein

570   I'm a godmother. That's a great thing to be, a godmother. She calls me god for short. That's cute. I taught her that. —Ellen DeGeneres

571   You know when you're young, you think your dad's Superman. Then you grow up and realize he's just a regular guy who wears a cape.
—Dave Atell

572   It is well to remember that the entire universe, with one trifling exception, is composed of others.   —John Andrew Holmes

573   It's just as sure a recipe for failure to have the right idea fifty years too soon as five years too late.
—J. R. Platt

574   Football incorporates the two worst elements of American society: violence punctuated by committee meetings.   —George Will

575   Education is a wonderful thing. If you couldn't sign your name you'd have to pay cash.
—Rita Mae Brown

576   Today it takes more brains to fill out the income tax form than it does to make the income.
—Alfred E. Neuman

577   Medicine: The only profession that labors incessantly to destroy the reason for its existence.
—James Bryce

ANSWERS

578 People always come up to me and say that my smoking is bothering them. Well it's killing me! —Wendy Liebman

579 I got the bill for my surgery. Now I know what those doctors were wearing masks for. —James H. Boren

580 Bigamy is having one husband too many. Monogamy is the same. —Erica Jong

581 Health—what my friends are always drinking to before they fall down. —Phyllis Diller

582 Whenever I feel like exercise, I lie down until the feeling passes. —Robert M. Hutchins

583 I have spent a lot of time searching through the Bible for loopholes. —W. C. Fields

584 The difference between divorce and legal separation is that a legal separation gives a husband time to hide his money. —Johnny Carson

585 If we could sell our experiences for what they cost us, we'd be millionaires. —Abigail Van Buren

586 Men can read maps better than women. 'Cause only the male mind could conceive of one inch equaling a hundred miles. —Roseanne Arnold

587 I called in sick today—but as soon as I hung up the phone, I felt a lot better. —Bunny Hoest and John Reiner

588 All the things I really like to do are either immoral, illegal, or fattening. —Alexander Woollcott

589 Women are repeatedly accused of taking things personally. I cannot see any other honest way of taking them. —Marya Mannes

590 No matter how happily a woman may be married, it always pleases her to discover that there is a nice man who wishes that she were not. —H. L. Mencken

591 My old boyfriend used to say, "I read *Playboy* for the articles." I used to say, "Right, I go to shopping malls for the music." —Rita Rudner

592 Is there a cure for a broken heart? Only time can heal your broken heart, just as time can heal his broken arms and legs. —Miss Piggy

593 There is no pleasure in having nothing to do; the fun is in having lots to do and not doing it. —Mary Wilson Little

594 A diplomat is a man who always remembers a woman's birthday but never remembers her age. —Robert Frost

595 The mark of a true crush … is that you fall in love first and grope for reasons afterward. —Shana Alexander

596 Marrying a man is like buying something you've been admiring for a long time in a shop window. You may love it when you get it home, but it doesn't always go with everything else. —Jean Kerr

597 The marvelous thing about a joke with a double meaning is that it can only mean one thing. —Ronnie Barker

ANSWERS

598   Income tax: It has made more liars out of American people than
golf.   —Will Rogers

599   I never knew what real happiness was until I got married. And by
then it was too late.   —Max Kauffmann

600   If you can't say anything good about someone, sit right here by me.
—Alice Roosevelt Longworth

INDEX

Numbers refer to the quote numbers, not the page numbers.